Bernard Kops'
East End

Bernard Kops
Dec 2006

Bernard Kops' East End

By the Waters of Whitechapel

Bernard Kops

Five Leaves Publications

www.fiveleaves.co.uk

Bernard Kops' East End
by Bernard Kops

Published in 2006 by Five Leaves Publications,
PO Box 9786, Nottingham NG1 9AW
info@fiveleaves.co.uk
www.fiveleaves.co.uk

ISBN: 1905512112
9781905512119

Five Leaves acknowledges financial support
from Arts Council England

Typeset and design by Four Sheets Design and Print
Printed in Great Britain by Russell Press

Five Leaves is a member of Inpress (www.inpressbooks.co.uk),
representing independent publishers

Contents

For Erica

Introduction

Bernard Kops' East End is published in celebration of the writer's eightieth birthday. But reaching eighty is no more an excuse to sink into slippers and cocoa than any other birthday. Bernard Kops is not long back from New York where his *Playing Sinatra* is in the early stages of production, and where he initiated a series of workshops with other writers. He has just finished a major play, an Arts Council commission, *Rogues and Vagabonds* — about travelling actors in the Yiddish theatre in Russia under the Czars. There will be a rehearsed reading initially before production. "I'll put a copy in the post — I think you'll love it," says Bernard. This follows his recent *Returning We Hear the Larks*, about the poet Isaac Rosenberg, and a play about Isaac Babel. A productive year.

I write this after our next-to-last meeting prior to publication of this book. We discussed whether there is time for him to finish some East End cameos to go into this collection. Maybe not, so how about a later pamphlet? And this war in Lebanon… "I never felt at home in Israel, I'm a European — I wanted to get back home. But it has to survive, even if their governments are all mad."

At eighty Bernard Kops is as enthusiastic about his work as half a century ago. A couple of weeks after the above conversation I get a note asking if this book could come out a bit early, he's doing some workshops in Dumfries, and, by the way, he's already fixed several readings in London.

Bernard Kops was born in 1926 in the East End of London, the son of Dutch-Jewish working class parents. In front of me is a copy of *Encore: the voice of vital theatre* of September/October 1958 which includes features on new authors. On the front cover is a photograph — reprinted below — of some of them: Arnold Wesker; Errol John; Bernard Kops; David Campton; NF Simpson; Harold Pinter; Ann Jellicoe; John Mortimer. Clive Goodwin, the editor, was clearly a good picker. Bernard Kops' first play *The Hamlet of Stepney Green* was a great success. Novels, plays, collections of poetry, and two volumes of autobiography followed over the next half-century.

Bernard Kops' creativity has certainly lasted longer than several of his publishers. MacGibbon and Kee, Coward-McCann and Scorpion exist within that peculiar publishers' half-life, cropping up on second-hand book-searches, while Secker survives only as part of an imprint of the monolithic Random House. This is as good a place as any then to thank Hearing Eye for keeping his poetry in print, and Oberon for reviving his plays. The novels, sadly, are currently unavailable save for the excerpts printed here, but the second volume of Bernard Kops' autobiography, *Shalom Bomb* is available from Oberon. A significant part of the first volume is re-issued here.

Bernard Kops has managed to fit a lot in: extreme poverty in childhood (not that he had much choice about fitting that in): selling books off a barrow: great writing success followed by failure; drug addiction and recovery; and that tremendous productivity as an artist. All of his books are dedicated to his wife Erica, who has been there through most of it with him.

Again and again Kops returns to his origins, in the Jewish East End — the theme of this collection. With Wesker and Pinter, and the next generation of Mike Leigh and Steven Berkoff, he stands in the first rank of Anglo-Jewish playwrights. This collection includes his most recent radio play, *The Lost Love of Phoebe Myers*, broadcast on Radio 4. This short play bears out Mike Leigh's remark about Bernard Kops that "Few writers, and even fewer dramatists have managed to explore so fully our inexhaustible capacity for trying to escape that endless series of traps called Life."

Ross Bradshaw, Five Leaves Publications

Back row:
*Arnold Wesker,
Errol John,
Bernard Kops
and David
Campton,*

Front row:
*N.F. Simpson,
Harold Pinter,
Ann Jellicoe and
John Mortimer*

Ballad of Bethnal Green

The dustmen were busy with the empty boxes, and the straw and water were now running along the gutters. The last hands of overripe bananas were being knocked out at ridiculous prices and goldfish were being quickly auctioned to the few remaining children. Ten minutes ago the whole area was crammed with people but now it was almost deserted. The traders were busy packing their unsold commodities back into the small vans.

"Ten bob a time, lovely bitches!" one man shouted, brushing the fur of the puppies forward, his eyes darting in all directions, on the lookout for the law.

A crying child stroked a shivering puppy but she couldn't bear to look at it; besides, her eyes were swimming in tears.

"You know we can't have him," her mother moaned. "You know dogs ain't allowed!"

The child sobbed and hugged the dog more tightly, then she put it back on the stall and followed her mother away. The water rushing along the streets swept away paper bags, the shrimp shells and the usual muck of Sunday and the last puppies were whisked from their saturated straw and soon everyone was gone, except the dustmen.

Sunday in Bethnal Green is always depressing when the markets close. A sickness descends, a horrible empty nostalgia, yet here I was again wandering through the back-streets, through the lonely, squashed, long grey streets, streets that were given colour only by faces of people. But now most of those faces are gone, though Brick Lane still stands. Brick Lane with its sweating walls and sweating ghosts.

I was on no romantic pilgrimage through the back streets of my past, but on my way to the hospital where my father was dying; but once snared by the streets, I had to walk past my old home. My father smoked a brand of tobacco that tobacconists didn't seem to stock any more. I tried five shops in the main road but they all shook their heads. For years we had all pleaded with him to smoke something that smelled sweeter, but who could begrudge him his own brand on his last days? I eventually found

First published in Queen's Magazine — *1960s.*

the tobacco in a boarded-up shop. The woman with whiskers remembered me though her face had gone clean out of my head. She seemed to know about my father.

"He shouldn't be smoking if he's got that." Then she asked me how my baby was getting on, and I told her that my son was now five and was going to school.

"That just shows how time flies, time flies." She went on about how everyone had moved away and all old faces were gone. And where were they all now? I thought, afraid for the moment to move out of a doorway, my eyes fixed on the windows of my old room.

They are gone to death or to the suburbs, gone to the cemetery, not far from here most of them, lying for all eternity under the smoky chimneys of Forest Gate, under the earth, under their Jewish stones. Soon my father will join them, and although married again he will lie in the space he has reserved beside my mother. It's so strange that he will die surrounded by nuns in the long white gowns, in a place known as a Hostel of God, which he believes is a hospital of recovery. It is in a way a place of recovery. Last week he said, 'This place suits me down to the ground.' I curled up inside but agreed with him. That was when my stepmother cried beside the bed and when he asked her why she was crying, she replied that she was cold. Holding on to life, we have an infinite capacity to pull the wool over our eyes.

So l stood there for a time under my old window where I did a lot of my growing up, a lot of my looking out and a great deal of my dreaming, dreaming into the dirty air, dreaming unformed dreams of no-one and nowhere. And once again I could see my mother leaning over the railings, throwing me down sixpence to go to the pictures, and this was the first time I had ventured here since she died, when I tore up all my poems and burned them, saying over and over again, 'Well, that's that! That's that!' When the family split into seven segments and I into a thousand.

It was the first Sunday in spring when I stood there, writing this, remembering the past that I hated and needed. The clouds were fast and it was cold so I walked towards Columbia Market. It was deserted and desolate as I stood by the incised monument, but the grime and the soot of a hundred years had already effaced the words commemorating that kinky but kind woman who had built the place. This sprawling, oppressive pseudo-Gothic dream that lay derelict, built to house the destitute, for here was the Old Nichol. Just a hundred years ago, people lived in squalor and died like flies.

Now remaining black stones waited for the men who would come with bulldozers, and all was loneliness as l walked into the guts of the tenement, disturbing a few slow pigeons who flapped their wings and whirred to the crumbling roof.

I walked up the stairs and I jumped as I came face to face with an old woman chopping wood on a landing. She backed away from me as I looked beyond her to one of the empty stinking rooms, of which she had obviously taken possession. Her face was smeared with smoke and her wrinkled stocking, more holes than cloth, revealed skin as black as the stones.

"WHAT DO YOU WANT?" she quickly croaked like a parrot.

"Nothing!" I replied.

"Well, you won't find it here!"

She scuttled inside and I hurried back to the playground that echoed only with the wind and with forgotten cries of dead children.

I wandered away, towards Shoreditch Church, wandered on to a bombsite behind the mission hospital, where high up from a back window a nun looked down at me. This was once called Sweet Apple Square. Here stood, or rather squatted, rows and rows of tiny Mongoloid Victorian houses. I remember the night when the land mine dropped and I remember the next morning when I looked out of the window. The houses and the people were all gone.

Laughter brought me back to the present and two boys came quickly towards me, hurtling down a slope on pram wheels. Lovely London boys wearing woollen Balaclavas on their heads with school caps perched above. Their pockets full of string and nails, badges on their lapels, grubby scratched knees and snotty noses. They punched each other and giggled.

"There was houses here once," one said.

"Really?" I replied, to draw them out.

"Straight up! But there was a war see, and a whacking bomb fell what killed everybody."

"You're kidding! I don't believe you," I replied.

Indignantly the other boy confirmed, told me that his dad told him and his dad wasn't a liar.

"Fowsands died! It was a big bomb."

"Oh yes, I remember now," I said and this pleased them; one

tugged at me, made me follow him over the stones.

"See! Houses! See the stone steps and there was a street here. See this stone kerb!"

"All the grass has grown over now," the other said. "We play here, find all sorts of fings, all sorts of smashing fings."

They told me they were fed up with the telly and their eyes were as excited as amateur archaeologists as they pottered about, pointing out tiles and floorboards, poking the ground with sticks.

"We find broken cups and saucers and sometimes even plates!"

I wasn't listening anymore. They had spoken to me as if I had not belonged to that past, yet here were the walls that had enclosed me. Here in these streets I played as a child, knocking down ginger and hide and seek, and here I laughed, not caring or knowing the chaos that surrounded me. And here I grew up and scratched my name with hearts and arrows into the walls, and opposite, in those buildings, I watched the bugs running out of holes and I let them alone because the smell of them crushed was even worse then the sight of them. Here was my home, and now it was part of history, and I was part of that past. And there were faces at those windows that were no longer there, faces of men and women as rotted as the dead of the plague and the fire. Faces that have gone into always, gone with their houses, houses as gone as those of Carthage and Pompeii.

Gone into the past forever the Bethnal Green I knew, and now only Queens Buildings, my old tenement, still stands, a dirty crumbling oasis surrounded by mounds of earth and mushrooming clinical contemporary blocks of flats. On those stairs I sat, in the darkness, finding out about the bodies of girls. Girls gone to Stamford Hill, Golders Green and Israel. Gone are the Jewish girls of Bethnal Green! Gone Lew the shoemaker, gone to the ground. Gone Mrs. Plotz from Minsk or Pinsk, who argued incessantly with my mother, and now lies not thirty yards from her, for ever. Neighbours in death. Gone Mrs. Lubin, gone Lionel, the boy who once handed me the first book of poems I ever read, the poems of T.S. Eliot.

"Read this!" he said.

Gone Doris, the girl who wanted to come to my sixteenth birthday party, but couldn't afford a present. "I'll give you myself," she said.

4

"Give me a sample, now," I begged, and she did, but she didn't let me go all the way down. I agreed that she could come to the party, but for some reason she never did, and I never saw her again. Gone Mr. Rubin and his sweet shop. Gone Mr. Adler the trouser-maker. Gone the sweatshops, gone the teeming, exciting, terrible, alive, dingy, dirty, marvellous, depressing streets.

"There was this bloke called Hitler, see..." The voices of the boys disturbed my thoughts but only for a second.

They spoke as if I couldn't have known, I who lived not a stone's throw from here, I who hid under stairs and passages, who rushed sometimes even faster than my ailing mother, to get into the shelter of the underground before her, I who heard Sweet Apple Square being pulverised and wiped off the world. I who saw the remains and destruction, who saw even a policeman weep as he carried out a dead child.

"We find broken cups and saucers..." The memory of what the boys had said a few minutes before echoed through my head. I tossed them two shillings.

"A shilling each!" I said as I turned to go.

"Cor! Fanks! Fanks, Mister!" They punched and hugged each other with delight, could hardly believe their luck, and they jumped and danced and shouted.

As they left I could see that the nun in the window had watched the proceedings. They rushed away from me, on the pram wheels, but they looked back several times and waved goodbye, like relatives. I never knew money could make people so happy. I never knew anything could make people so happy, any more.

They will build on that site soon, the bulldozers will come and the builders will come and more new clean regular segments will arise. Honeycombs of office blocks and apartments. Another layer of people will be pushed under; another thin, tenuous layer of civilisation will be pushed into history. I with my tenement will go into the school books of those boys. I with my scratched heart and my arrows and bugs already belong in the past.

And we will be known as the age of broken cup and saucer, the age of the broken child and broken heart.

———————————

Passover '38

One thing I remember
even more than the hunger.
Scrubbing my knees, smarting my hair and
rushing downstairs
into that playground of my childhood;
where all the other children
with their eyes alight
were building castles with crackernuts.

I built my castle.
I was a shopkeeper, a millionaire,
I ruled the world;
challenging all to chance
nuts of their own,
gathered from high pitched aunts
the day before,
as we went from home to home,
running that *Yomtov* gauntlet
of twisted cheeks and wet kisses.

In those days families extended forever and ever.

Who wants a castle?
Knock down my castle! I dared.
All in their sudden beauty
the girls came singing, flirting.
Holiday! Passover!
The Angel of Death? Who is he?
a madman on the radio, far away.

Passover lasted for the rest of the year;
the crackernuts secure
in the lining of my sleeve.
Belonging — we belonged.

Poverty came later,
when most of us did well
and moved away.

From *Barricades in West Hampstead* (1988)

Whitechapel Library, Aldgate East

How often I went in for warmth and a doze
The newspaper room whilst my world outside froze
And I took out my sardine sandwich feast.
Whitechapel Library, Aldgate East.
And the tramps and the madman and the chattering crone.
The smell of their farts could turn you to stone
But anywhere, anywhere was better than home.

The joy to escape from family and war.
But how can you have dreams?
You'll end up on the floor.
Be like your brothers, what else is life for?

You're lost and you're drifting, settle down, get a job.
Meet a nice Jewish girl, work hard, earn a few bob.
Get married, have kids; a nice home on the never
and save for the future and days of rough weather.

Come back down to earth, there is nothing more.
I listened and nodded, like I knew the score.
and early next morning I crept out the door.

Outside it was pouring.
I was leaving forever.

I was finally, irrevocably done with this scene,
The trap of my world in Stepney Green.
With nowhere to go and nothing to dream

A loner in love with words, but so lost
I wandered the streets, not counting the cost.

I emerged out of childhood with nowhere to hide,
when a door called my name
And pulled me inside.

From *Grandchildren and Other Poems* (2000)

And being so hungry I fell on the feast.
Whitechapel Library, Aldgate East.

And my brain explodes when I suddenly find
an orchard within for the heart and the mind.
The past was a mirage I'd left far behind

And I am a locust and I'm at a feast.
Whitechapel Library, Aldgate East.

And Rosenberg also came to get out of the cold
To write poems of fire, but he never grew old.
And here I met Chekov, Tolstoy, Meyerhold.
I entered their worlds, their dark visions of gold.

The reference library, where my thoughts were to rage.
I ate book after book, page after page.
I scoffed poetry for breakfast and novels for tea.
And plays for my supper. No more poverty.
Welcome young poet, in here you are free
to follow your star to where you should be.

That door of the library was the door into me.

And Lorca and Shelley said "Come to the feast."
Whitechapel Library, Aldgate East.

from **The World is a Wedding**
Child in the Family

Take one Jew and immediately you have an opposition party. In our family it was no exception. Our home was like a Yiddisher parliament, with seven opposition parties. Plus my mother and father, who were trying to govern and be in the opposition at the same time. Each of us constantly talked, fifty to the dozen, trying to be heard, pulling each other's garments, arms, and even faces, to make the others listen. And we shouted most of the time, mainly to ourselves. There was always someone laughing or crying at any given moment.

We each lived in our own world, except for my mother who lived in all our worlds, But each of our worlds was held together by our home in Stepney Green. Twenty-three, Stepney Green Buildings — right at the top of seven flights, a red-brick tenement erected eighty or so years ago.

There were seven children sharing two beds in that buggy attic, two single beds, beds without sheets, whose springs scratched our bodies, springs that were victims of relentless pillow-fights and our jumping up and down. From the windows I could see as far as Tower Bridge, its arms opening and closing several times a day, as if welcoming in new immigrants.

My father had come from Amsterdam, from poverty, and he settled near the docks, like most of the Jews before him, who stayed near the river, I suppose, to keep as close as possible to the Old Country. On his first morning in London he got on a tram in the Mile End Road and said to everyone, "Good morning all", the only words of English he knew. They ignored him, thought he was mad.

A couple of weeks later he met my mother in Forest Gate, of all places. She too came from a Dutch Jewish family, though slightly better off than his. They married at the synagogue in Stepney Green, both of them about five feet three inches tall — though later they shrank to five feet. My mother's width, however, made up for her height.

From *The World is a Wedding,* autobiography (1963)

9

The first war brought a certain physical prosperity, and my father, a leather-worker, made jerkins for soldiers. That sort of prosperity seems to go with war; for when the war finished so did work. I was born in the middle of the General Strike. My father, prolific in giving my mother children, seemed to be the only one not on strike. All those days were a tremendous struggle to get money, a struggle largely falling on the shoulders of my mother, who lived for each moment, scheming and dreaming — who, in the words of mothers of her sort, and though not actually believing in God, would often say: "God is good, something will turn up." But the only thing that seemed to turn up was more children and more poverty.

My first concrete memory was waiting for a new child to arrive. My sister Phoebe, my brother Dave and myself were sitting on the stairs eating ice-cream cornets. This was a rare treat, so something obviously was up, and we knew my father had given us the money to get out of the house. I had heard my mother moaning during the day, from the bedroom; but because I had been told the usual stupid stories about the stork, the gooseberry bush and the doctor's little black bag, I asked my sister why she needed to go on so. The doctor came shuffling up the stairs, and as he passed us Phoebe said, "The baby's in that case."

"I know — I can see the arms and the legs sticking out."

She told me not to be so silly, so I rejected the case theory, and the stork came back into favour. When we went inside the house we all thought it a great giggle, because Marie, my eldest sister, told us we would all be eating upstairs in our room.

My mother moaned throughout the night, and I kept awake until the dawn. When I went into her room, I expected to see feathers all over the place. There was my mother, and Rose.

"God bless you," my mother said to me.

"Yes. He does owe me something," I would like to think I replied.

There were seven of us. I was the seventh, but Rose was the eighth child. The first had died at the age of three, and lay buried in a little Christian cemetery in Leicester, in a special corner that had been consecrated Jewish, just for her. I often thought of her lying there, all alone, and I remember my mother crying about her quite often. "To lose a parent is the worst thing in the world; but to lose a child is even worse."

10

Despite her obsessive involvement with us, my mother tried to emulate the birds. She loved her children, lived for us and through us, tried to provide for us, to prepare us for flight, to provide us with the strength to reject her. But blood is very much thicker than water in a Jewish family. One day my melancholic Aunt Esther came, my father's eldest sister. I could hear them having a row. Aunt Esther was childless, but she had some money saved, and she chided us on our poverty. "I've got the quids," she said.

"And I've got the kids," my mother replied, equally as nasty. But neither of them had other weapons to use. Aunt Esther died in a mad house. When they went through her furniture, they found millions of pieces of paper that had been torn up methodically. Nobody knew why.

There were no books in my house. Lots of laughter and language, but no books. Except the dreaded rent book, and the insurance book — for my parents, no matter how hard-up they were, were already insuring themselves against the day when they would die, so that they wouldn't be a burden upon us, and there would be enough money to pay for the ground, the coffin and the stone. But books weren't missed, because they never occurred to me. Hunger did — and not only the hunger for food, which was bad enough, but the hunger for things that I couldn't fathom.

My father was unemployed and on the means test, and was somehow expected, God knows how, to bring us up on twenty-eight shillings a week. A woman who lived nearby sometimes brought us in potatoes. She worked 'Up West', my mother told me — 'Up West' was that fabulous world beyond, our Eldorado. It was only years later that I guessed what sort of work the woman did — for who in the Buildings could afford to give their neighbours potatoes in those days?

Yet it was a happy childhood, almost idyllic, and I was practically the happiest child of the whole family. I used to enjoy running around to my aunt's to try to borrow a shilling. My father would bring the money from the Labour Exchange on Friday; it was gone by Sunday, and by Monday my mother was already on the borrow. So when my father came with money on the Friday, most of it had to be paid back. A pair of shoes, or the one good suit in the family, or the wedding ring, was the pawnable article. And I used to love to go to the pawnshop with

11

my mother, though she hated it. Everyone was pawning; yet everyone was ashamed of it. I suppose that's why the pawning entrance was always tucked away. Soon as we entered the pawnshop, the man knew exactly how much to give us, and would hand us the money even before the shoes were on the counter. With the few shillings would come a certain relief to my mother's face, and she'd always sing me the same song on the way home:

> *Mary, Mary, at the pawnshop door,*
> *A bundle in her hand and a parcel on the floor*
> *She asked for seven-and-six but they only gave her four,*
> *So she pulled the blinkin' handle off the pawnshop door.*

We would sometimes get food parcels from the Jewish Board of Guardians: demerara sugar, butter beans, and margarine. Now I come to think of it, a strange combination. And meat, bread, and coal tickets from another Jewish organisation. But there were so many Jewish families in the same position that this help was very spasmodic. In winter we used to burn old shoes in the fireplace, and I would often search the streets, where the sight of a solitary, dirty shoe would be like a gift of manna. Shoes, in the streets of the East End, were few and far between.

And I would go with my father to the soup kitchens. We'd walk all the way to Aldgate with a saucepan, and return with pea soup and black bread, after waiting hours in the queue, the long queue of tired, hungry people. I remember a friend suddenly didn't want to speak to me any more, so I collared him one day and asked him why. He said that he had actually seen my father eating the soup at the soup kitchen. I denied it indignantly, said, "We never eat it there — we always bring it home!" Apparently, and for the life of me I can't see the reason, to have your soup there wasn't considered nice. This strange snobbery existed in all manner of things, even though we were all in it together. For instance, my mother hated to be seen taking me to the Jewish Board of Guardians, where I would receive clothing, clothing I needed desperately, clothing that everybody else also got, smelling of moth balls, clothing of the most wonderful cloth, but often five sizes too large for me, handed down by wealthy Jews the other side of nowhere.

It was a self-imposed ghetto, but a happy world. And there was a spirit of community as in a village. People were involved in each other's lives, and not for the wrong reasons. Now, looking back, I see it was a desperate time — but then it meant security, and happiness. It was my world, and Aldgate East was the outside frontier of that world, a world that consisted mainly of Jewish people. I had no chip on my shoulder about being Jewish, because I knew of nothing else that existed. The teeming streets sheltered the family, and poverty wasn't imposed by economics or society. It was just something to battle against.

Stepney Green was wide open, with a narrow park running the length of it, with trees that had stood there for perhaps a hundred years. My mother said she remembered the cows grazing there, although I believe they grazed only in her imagination.

My parents were not religious. My mother lit the candles on Friday because she said it was nice, and on this night we would have a proper meal. My father said poor people couldn't afford to be religious; yet we followed the Jewish festivals, and ceremony broke into the stark reality of day-to-day living. On Passover all the children of the Buildings used to play with cracker-nuts in the playground, building little castles of nuts, and knocking them down with more nuts. And we would go from one aunt to another on these occasions, perhaps to show off a new pair of socks, and they would give us an orange, an apple, or sweets. It was worth running the gauntlet for such gifts: I say gauntlet, because visiting my aunts entailed being pinched on the cheeks until we were almost black-and-blue, them saying atavistically, "You're so lovely I could eat you" or "I could pinch you to bits". Kosher cannibalism.

On *Succoth*, or *Simchat Torah*, we would go from one synagogue to the next, queuing up for bags of sweets and fruit, often receiving a gift, then going to the back of the queue again.

Already, before I had even started school, the religious people tried to claim me, tried to make me go to the Hebrew classes, and the Hebrew teachers were far stricter than anyone I had met up till then. My mother agreed that I should go, perhaps to get me out of the way. So I went once or twice, to the *cheder* in Redmans Road. But the Hebrew symbols were meaningless to me, and the call of the streets was stronger than the call of God. So I played truant.

13

One day the Hebrew master was at the door, calling about my absence. I hid under the table. He came in and stood with his legs apart in a pompous pose: "What about his Hebrew education, his Bar Mitzvah?"

"Would that butter his bread?" my father replied. "A poor boy can't afford to be religious."

The street door was open; so I rushed through the man's legs, and flew down the seven flights of stairs, four at a time, and into the streets.

A little while later I was not able to use my legs so freely. I developed rickets — and my legs went into irons. They stayed on for a month or so, but my mother wanted to take them off.

"If you do," the doctor said at the Jewish hospital, "his legs will fall away from under him."

My mother took the irons off nevertheless; and I was soon running through the streets again. My mother trusted no-one and nothing, except her instinct.

I played outside in the park, with my brothers and sisters, and the Lever children, and on one Saturday morning there happened the first tragedy in my life. A man had been coming around regularly with a magnifying glass. He'd catch the rays of the sun and burn pieces of paper, and we'd all stand around to watch the flames. We were drawn to that man; even though time and time again we had been warned not to go near him. On this Saturday morning he burned the paper as usual, and touched us all, boys and girls, between the legs. The next moment a policeman was gripping hold of him and pulling him away. We followed him as he was being dragged along the Green. I couldn't understand why the policeman was hurting him so much, all because of a magnifying glass and a few pieces of paper.

We played a lot in that park: hop-scotch and 'Poor Jenny is a-weeping'. My mother's name was Jenny, I thought they were connected. We were often too busy to go upstairs for food, and sometimes she would throw me down a crust of bread in a paper bag.

"Mum-eeee! Throw me down a ha'penn-eee!" I called up. And she would come to the railings and shake her head. A ha'penny was gold dust in those days.

I used to search the little streets for money, and remember thinking that if I walked on one side of the road I might miss it on the other side. But once I did find sixpence, and I flew up the stairs to give it to my mother. It was those stairs, those seven flights, that ruined her, that crippled her health and eventually led to her death. Those flights that she went up and down three or four times a day, stopping at each landing for several minutes to catch her breath, on her endless journeys to find a couple of shillings from somewhere or other.

"When I'm rich I'll take you to Torquay," I used to say. I thought Torquay was somewhere in the tropics. But I never took her anywhere.

All my aunts and uncles and cousins were poor, except one uncle who won some money on the Irish Sweepstakes. He would drive up once a year in his Rolls Royce, all the kids of the area would surround the car, and the chauffeur would open the door, and my little uncle would trot up the stairs, puffing on his cigar. He would give my mother a kiss and a pound note, and we would line up for sixpence each. A yearly ceremony, where my mother would cry tears of gratitude, and off he'd trot again, down to his car.

My father was almost blind, and bad eyes don't improve with the sort of work he was doing. A clicker gets his name from the sound that the knife makes as it clicks around the pattern and into the leather. And when he did work, his face had been getting closer and closer to the bench, and his hands were getting slower and slower. I remember the day he cried. The sound of my father crying was one of the worst sounds in the world. He just lay on the floor and wept. Women's tears were easy to cope with; after all, I had four sisters. But we all stood around him, not knowing what to do.

Apparently the boss's son came to my father's workbench and said, smiling, "Mr Kops you've worked very hard in your life, and we think it's about time you had a little rest." My dad was delighted to hear this, thinking perhaps they were going to send him to some philanthropic clickers' convalescent home.

"So we're going to give you an extra week's money. And here are your unemployment cards," Then it dawned on the old man that he had just been given the sack, after thirteen years with the same firm.

"The toe-rag, the lousy rotten toe-rag!" my father moaned on the floor.

"Toe-rag" was the worst thing that he could call anyone. Although I never felt close to him, I must admit that he was a tryer. Afterwards he went to race meetings, to sell lemonade and chocolate. And I journeyed out of the East End for the first time, went with him to Epsom to collect empty bottles to get the deposit money, and to scratch out the prices on the bars of chocolate for him to sell at a higher price. On the way home we'd buy food, returning in a sort of triumph, in those desperate times.

During the holidays we were all at home. All under my mother's feet, when she would sing, sardonically, "How I wish it was Sunday every day" — or she'd say, "That's all I'm short of. Some holiday I've got." To get away I would sometimes go to the synagogue along the road, purely to drink from the goblet of wine. Not that I wasn't caught up in the ceremony, for whilst mouthing my fake Hebrew I found myself *dovening*, swaying backwards and forwards as my ancestors had done for thousands of years. I tried to stop but it was impossible so I gave myself up to it.

"Religion's a lot of tommy rot," my father said time and time again, but I noticed that he loved being involved in the main ceremonies of birth, marriage and death. When my young cousin died I saw mourning close up for the first time. The family arriving with cakes and chocolate, trying to cheer up the immediate family who sat on cut-down chairs. The mirrors were covered, the men were unshaven and a woman walked round the room cutting the sleeves of the closest relatives with a razor blade.

"What's that for?" asked my father.

"The rending of the garments."

"Why do they sit so low down?"

'To be close to the earth. Shush!"

"Why the mirrors covered?"

"So that we don't see our own sorrow, to stop vanity. Now shut up!" Then he prayed with the others and just as fervently. My father was a strange atheist. Although very much bound up with the family and with life my parents were very much tied to the dead. My mother's constant expressions were, "I swear by my mother in the grave"; "may I drop dead on this spot if I'm not telling the truth"; "may I get run over and smashed." Sometimes if she was cold she would shudder and say, "someone walked over my grave".

About the time that my cousin died a bird flew from one of the trees onto our landing. It was injured and I took it inside but it escaped and fluttered away from me. It clung to the guard around the fireplace, and then it fell off — and I accidentally trod on it. It lay dead, and I cried. My mother told me to throw it down the lavatory. "Where does it go to, the lavatory?" I asked.

"Why, to the river." She replied, and my sadness gave way to wonder and I suddenly became aware that my house was attached to the river, and the river was attached to the world. That day a man came to fix the electricity in the house. We were all so excited we switched the light on, hundreds of times, on and off. "Let them get on with it, ma," the man said, "they'll soon get fed up with it." And we did.

But though we used to play together we all had our different worlds. Marie was serious, went regularly to the Brady Street Girls Club — Essie, the blonde little temptress, a little Mae West they used to call her, we had a photograph in sepia to prove it — and Jack, up in the bedroom being a Gentleman of Japan, rehearsing The Mikado for some local Operatic Society, before that he used to write monologues and practice them. There he was strangling himself with his hand clutching his throat and his tongue hanging out while we all watched with horror and pride. "Why should I have to hang on the end of a rope, the rope! The Rope! AAAAhhhh!" Carrol Levis was king in those days, on Radio Luxembourg; *Stardust* would play and his soft Canadian voice would say "The discoveries of today are the stars of tomorrow". And every poor boy's dream was to be discovered and to escape and be good to his parents. Jack actually got an audition but nothing more was heard. A little later he stopped strangling himself and settled down.

Phoebe was slightly distant, in her moody brooding world — Dave, in the other bedroom, all alone — being cricketer, bowler, referee, umpire and commentator all at the same time, and Rose, toddling around in that gooey, cooey world of babies. I used to love playing with candles and poking the fire, seeing cities and forests and people in the flames.

"You'll wet the bed." My mother said. I don't know where my mother got her superstitions from — she was one of the most superstitious women alive. If one of us swallowed something and it went down the wrong hole, she'd say, "Look up, and turn round three times" or "spit out and go to the lavatory" or "look down and close your eyes and count fifteen." It usually worked. It must have come direct from the Middle Ages.

All the time I wanted to know about my parent's past — where our ancestors came from but I could never get much out of them except a few details about their grandparents, and that was that.

But whereas the others were quite content to accept those few details, and the world around them, I wanted to know how I fitted into the order of things, wanted to discover my roots and establish some sort of identity. I used to lie awake at night, long after everyone else had said goodnight, and watch the progress of the bugs up the wall. Though I'd squash the fleas upon me, I could never crush the bugs, because the smell of them was even more repulsive than the sight of them. We were so ashamed of those bugs; yet one night I overcame my repulsion and looked at them as creatures, little miracles.

"Bern," Phoebe would call over. "You still awake?"

"Yes — what do you want?" I was miles away. Not in that room, not in the East End, not in England or even the world.

"What you thinking of?"

"Nothing," I'd reply. "What you thinking of?"

"Nothing also. Good-night."

"Good-night."

We were always close. Phoebe was always called a little mother, though once she did drop me down a flight of stairs when I wet her. Maybe that explains why I became so different.

The boats moaned on the river, sounding like prehistoric monsters at a feast. And the trains shunted endlessly through the night like giants pinioned in a prison cell, hitting their manacles with their manacles, filling the dark with hollow clangs. I would lie awake dreaming of travel, feeling sick when I thought of eternity, and cry myself to sleep thinking of death, of my death, my pillow wet with tears.

"When I die it's for ever and ever and ever and ever."

Coats on the door would frighten me, and I'd pull the bedclothes right over my head. I've slept like that ever since.

But life was too funny and too serious for me to be entirely lost in dreaming; and most of the comedy and tragedy took place in the home, and then amongst my cousins and uncles and aunts. We were a very close, almost too close, family. Most of our cousins were double cousins, because the Kopses, those who came to England, the brothers and sisters — married their equivalent number amongst the Zetters. One whole family

18

married another. The Kopses were a serious, moral, almost melancholy lot, who saw sorrow and despair everywhere, looked always on the black side of things. If you said, "It's raining outside," they'd reply, "I suppose it will get much worse." They were never happy unless they were miserable. But the Zetters were an entirely different kettle of fish: good-looking, tending to over-optimism and living beyond their means. They were mainly gamblers, either working as tic-tac men on the racetracks or as bookmakers at the Hackney Wick dog stadium. They were fast talkers and I always found them most attractive, especially when they excitedly described the events of each race meeting, for every racing day carried its own inquest. The Zetters were never lost for ideas and were always looking for an opportunity to make a few bob, such as going from door to door and buying old gold and flogging it in the street markets on Sunday.

One of my uncles, I forget from which side of the family, tried to commit suicide in Whitechapel Station. He drank a bottle of disinfectant in the lavatory. Fortunately for him a porter heard the bottle crash to the floor as my uncle crumpled up. And even more fortunately, the London Hospital was opposite.

The Kopses were clean and practical, and liked food in their bellies. But the Zetters always seemed to dress smartly even though their bellies were empty. All sorts of dramas and intrigues were going on all the time at any family gathering. One could always see the women whispering across to each other or mouthing words across the room, and gasps of exasperation and surprise. I could never make out what it was all about.

I was a little older by the time another cousin died, a girl called Doris. She developed meningitis suddenly, a beautiful girl full of life, who used to sing, and she was singing right up till the last moment. Her voice belted out from the hospital ward, and was heard right across Stepney Green, singing, "Si, si, si, that South American Joe." My mother said she caught it washing her hair, so consequently we all stopped washing our hair for a long time.

I heard the word "Hitler" one day, heard my mother and my aunt cursing him. At first I thought he was an uncle out of favour. But my father told me he was our enemy, in another country, who wanted to destroy us all. Every so often after reading the newspapers my mother and my aunt would have a session of cursing.

"A *broch* on his *kishkas!*"

"A *crenk* on his brain!"

"May he get run over and smashed!"

"May he lack salt!"

"May he lose more blood than sea in the ocean!"

"May all his teeth fall out except one, and may he have the most terrible toothache in that one!"

It became a regular slanging match to see who could curse the worst. But it didn't do any good. The newspapers contained pictures of Jews being held up to ridicule by a jeering crowd, or a Jewish child scrubbing a road. My mother cried. "When I lost my daughter I cried enough tears to swim from here to America. I thought I had no tears left — and here I am crying again."

I began to get afraid, and I brooded. All the other children seemed to be springing up, and I was the smallest, reaching no higher than the table. When we ate we were not all served together: my father and the baby came first, and then the children, from the eldest downwards. I watched the cabbage and the potatoes disappearing in the pot, and practically panicked that it would all be gone before it was my turn. I stood next to my mother at the gas stove, trying to pinch the food as it was being cooked. Sometimes now I wonder whether the artist or the clown doesn't in fact emerge out of fear and sadness, out of trying to prove something to someone, or himself, out of the desire to be noticed. "Hey! Save some potatoes for me!" I never remembered my mother eating — though her weight never decreased.

I remember going with her along the river. It was Bank Holiday, and we were off to the Downs at Purley. Under the Rotherhithe Tunnel I clutched her and screwed up my eyes. "If you don't worry, I won't worry," I said to her. But I was terribly worried — and in a way I think she liked my fear, and I resented that, and felt guilty because I did. I used to love to smell her hair.

She was an ordinary woman who was extraordinary to me. When words got too much for her she'd just sit down and sigh or cry or sing, all the old songs: "When your hair has turned to silver, I will love you just the same," or "You die if you worry, you die if you don't, so why worry at all, it's only worry that killed the cat, anybody can tell you that." But this didn't stop her from worrying. She had a most terrible fear of the elements — if it started to rain she'd scream for us to come home, and if it thundered she'd unplug the wireless, hide the knives and forks and take all seven of us into the dark passage underneath the stairs. She told us we must always beware of strange people in the streets; "People will try to take you away," she warned us constantly. I would often wander out in the hope that they would.

In those strange rationalisations of Jewish people, she always expected things to turn out for the best, though experience proved to her time and time again that they didn't. To her, rich people were poor people with money, whereas her riches were seven children.

I played in the playground of the Buildings, and heard the children next door at the Jewish school singing Hebrew hymns, and reciting their multiplication tables. I knew my time was approaching and I dreaded the day. I was still bed-wetting, but somehow being so small and not going to school still gave me some excuse for doing that. Meanwhile, I organised the kids of my own age in that grey rectangle of stone that we called a playground, and under the stairs I played with Sarah and Anita from 'B' block, nearly always at hospitals. One day the girl downstairs said, "I'll show you mine if you show me yours." I undid my flies for her to see, but she didn't reciprocate — and I hated her, and didn't speak to her ever again.

With Sarah it was more idyllic. We lay on the floor together, behind the settee in her house, me pouring water into her vagina, or poking matchsticks into it, and she instinctively touching the thing I had only used for peeing with. She turned on me, however, and downstairs in the park told a gathering of children what I had done to her. I felt so ashamed, my whole world collapsed. Of course I denied it completely — I think she never forgave me for that. Everyone always said that we would get married, but I haven't seen her for almost twenty years.

About that time I played a lot with my cousin Derek. One day for no reason we took a goldfish out of a bowl and cut it in half with the scissors. This led to other excesses. I used to sit on the lavatory sometimes for half an hour.

"Have you fallen down the hole?" Various members of my family would call out at odd intervals. And I'd pretend to be straining. But I was catching flies with my hand and throwing them into a spider's web. I used to like to see the fly struggling and kicking, and the spider close in and surround it with silver thread. Other times I would hit flies with newspapers until I thought they were dead, then I'd pour a mound of salt over them and watch them come to life again.

But I wasn't only cruel. From off the mulberry leaves near the Buildings I collected silkworms, kept them, or I'd look for hairy caterpillars in front of the park and nest them in matchboxes. And I became very worried about the children in Duckett Street and Paragon Mansions, for they were in a far worse state than we were, with no shoes or socks, running sores on their faces, staring through the railings or standing on their stinking stairs. I became aware of a world far worse off than my own.

Every Sabbath my mother got out the only linen, and we'd manage to have some *lokshen* soup, and then we'd all play cards or have a sing-song. But I would sit by the window more often now, counting the church spires and watching Tower Bridge.

My mother hardly ever went out but I well remember the night she did go. There was an election going on, and the voting vans were going through the streets, the microphones promising God knows what, we who never had it, hadn't got it, and were never likely to get it. I could hear, "Vote for Doctor O'Donovan, for better conditions!" I jumped up at the window, and when I jumped down again the sewing machine collapsed on my head. Afraid that I might get told off, I jumped under the table. My sister Essie, delegated to look after us, pulled me out and rubbing my head, found that her hand was covered with blood. I was rushed to the Jewish hospital where I received seven stitches in my scalp, and a penny from the doctor for not crying.

When my mother came home that night it was so quiet she knew something was wrong. Six white faces stood there, and then she realised I was missing.

"Where's my Bernie? Where's my Bernie?"

She rushed to the bedroom where I, with an even whiter face, was sitting propped up, very proud of myself, my head swathed in bandages, building castles with playing cards.

"I'm never going out again," she said. "The one time I go out and look what happens! I'm never going out again." And I don't think she did, not by herself. She just stayed with her family, watching and worrying.

When I recovered, I started school.

* * *

22

Boy in the World

I hated school. Every morning for more than a year I think I cried — and when I saw that crying wouldn't work, I pretended to be ill. I worked through every illness that I knew about, mostly protesting that I had a sore throat. One morning I pretended that I had lost my voice, and put up such an act that my mother believed me. And when the school had gone in, I smiled smugly, and snuggled in bed as I heard the children in the hall of the school singing the usual patriotic song. But to my horror my mother *schlapped* me to the hospital. To my amazement they found that I had tonsilitis, I don't think I pretended after that.

Each dawn brought an empty feeling of dread and I dragged myself unwillingly towards the infants' class. The Hebrew and everything else that they taught me went through one ear and out the other. All I longed for was the bell, to rush into the streets, back into the world. For I, being rejected by my brother and his gang, had now accumulated a gang of my own. There was Angel, and Gerald Lever, and Maxie Dyas. We had our own secret calls, our own secret code, and our own secret signs and our own invisible ink made of lemon juice. We played hide-and-seek or whizzed round the streets on our home-made scooters, chasing through the foggy nights, only returning to the base when we heard the call: "Allee in, we ain't a-playing!"

My brother, seeing that I had made a success of my own gang, now condescended to let me join his, which I did with considerable pleasure, and apparent indifference. Dave and I would now often play together, tying people's legs together under the table or unwinding a reel of cotton all round the floor. Sometimes we'd go to the sweetshop opposite, where he would engage Mr Lindsberg in conversation while I tried to pinch little cubes of chocolate. My mother found out, and I thought she would knock me across the room, but she didn't. She only shook her head and wept a little. We promised not to do it again, and we didn't.

Outside the Stepney Jewish school stood Esther the sweet woman, who I think did more business than Mr Lindsberg. She was an excitable widow who never used one word when twelve would do and she sold sweets from a battered pram, and stuck lollipops and lucky bags into the park railings. She was the Queen, the fearsome Empress, and most of our fantasies and dreams revolved around her pram. She chastised us as if she was doing us a big favour in serving us. Oh, the magic of that pram — the almond whirls and the sugar twirls, the chocolate kisses and sherbet fountains, the liquorice sticks and the hundreds and thousands, the stick-jaws and the gob-stoppers, the aniseed balls and the bullseyes.

One day when school was out, and she was pushing the pram away, I and my friends taunted her. "Why ain't you got a baby, Esther, in that pram?" She turned and chased us.

The East End was full of characters, full of people crying their wares — the Indian toffee-man: "Indian toffee, good for the belly, ask your mummy for a penny, and buy some Indian toffee!" Even if I had a penny my mother wouldn't let me buy any — she said it was poisoned. "That's the way they carry children off to India!" But I used to love to watch him smiling with gold teeth and throwing the coloured sugar into the whining silver bowl, and see the pink floss being spun onto the wooden sticks. And the toffee apple man, with I swear five hundred toffee apples attached to a contraption on his head. And the muffin man with his bell, and the woman selling lavender: "Who will buy my sweet scented lavender? Sixteen branches for only one penny."

Not so long ago, yet gone forever.

The man who came with a small roundabout, painted the colours of the rainbow, and for some old clothes he'd give you a ride. I once offered him my socks, but he told me not to be so daft. And those men who came around the streets calling for old iron and lumber, who came with goldfish for old clothes. Why did they want old clothes, I thought. Who'd want the old clothes that we'd throw away? Even though I never remembered my mother throwing anything away.

People used to go into the streets in those days both during the day and in the evenings. The Mile End Waste was always crowded with people looking for bargains, and I liked to watch the people looking for bargains. The women were looking for bargains of food, the men looking for bargains of razor blades and shaving soap, the children looking for bargains of sweets, and the young men looking for bargains amongst the girls. I ventured away from the gang, and out of Stepney Green, and I wandered along the main Mile End Road, asking people for cigarette cards. And I'd forget that I was drifting, being so entirely caught up in the world around me: the old *Bubayachnas*, jawing on the doorsteps, talking about the price of fish, reading letters from relatives in Russia, often crying; talking their strange mixture of Yiddish and Cockney. They would say what they had to in Yiddish, and then completely repeat it in Cockney — pidgin English. But some of the old women, including Mrs Marovitz from another block, had been in England more than forty years, and still she could speak no more than three words of English.

I dawdled through the street markets, watching jewellery being haggled over, and thousands of herrings being pulled from their barrels and sliced by men whose fingers looked just like herrings. The streets behind Whitechapel fed me with a new sustenance: Old Montague Street, and Black Lion Yard, where the out-of-work tailors congregated on the corners, discussing politics, religion, money and politics, until someone would rush up: "I've got work for two men for two days!" Everyone would crowd forward, the men would be chosen, and the remainder would return to the discussion of politics.

Old men with beards, sitting outside Whitechapel church, eternally reliving the Russian revolution. Men stood around everywhere, anywhere, outside the kosher restaurant or the Turkish bath, or the Labour Exchange. Arguing was their occupation and you would have thought that they would soon be hitting each other — but instead they'd pat each other on the back and most reluctantly tear themselves away when midnight approached.

I caught snatches of their conversation as I stood near, trying to squeeze myself into the wall, so that I shouldn't be seen.

"Now Trotsky said to Lenin..." They'd speak as if they had the whole inside story. "And I said to Kropotkin..."

"Gorky said to me..."

"But Trotsky was a *nudnik*."

"Tenk God for communism!"

"Then why did you run away from Russia, Mr Gold?"

"To get away from my wife. But I have infinite faith in Stalin." He said this as if that was all the Russian dictator needed.

But across the road the scene wasn't so attractive. In Fieldgate Street there was an endless queue of ragged, expressionless men outside the Labour Exchange.

"Beigels! Beigels!" the old woman called from the corner of Brick Lane, with her dim, fat daughter sitting on the opposite corner. She shrieked incessantly, oblivious to everything around her. Along the Waste in the evenings the naphtha flares lit up the stalls, and sometimes a trader would hand me a blood orange or an over-ripe banana. And even though my mother had warned me, "Don't take nothing from no-one," the temptation was usually too great.

There was a sense of security in those days, despite the poverty. The communal feeling brought out the very best in the people of the East End. There was no question of keeping up with the Cohens, and there was no chase for gadgets. We were all in the same boat, children of the same onion boat. And I cannot remember the excitable neurosis that pervades bourgeois Jewish communities today. There were girls and the boys, flirting along Whitechapel High Street, fabulous girls with black eyes, eyes so beautiful, so alive, that one didn't notice the patched clothes. And the boys, larking about, running in and out of them, the girls giggling — and all of them queueing outside John Isaac's for chips.

There was a much wider use of language, a far more clever gift of the gab heard in those streets, when people were thrown onto themselves and each other. People talked to each other. Perhaps it was because they came from families, large families, where they were not fed on predigested stodge. The struggle had an exciting side each day, when a mother could put her children to bed with a little supper in their bellies was a fresh achievement.

A light came into our lives, a young man by the name of Ivor, who wore plus fours, a perpetual smile, and courted my sister Essie. My mother made us all leave the living room, and we'd all be whispering around in the passages or on the stairs while they cuddled on the settee. He came from Jubilee Street, from a well-off Russian Jewish family. His father was a cooper. Ivor was a god to me. He brought fruit to the house — fruit! We who couldn't afford potatoes were suddenly eating pears and oranges.

The children all lived, talked and dreamed about him. He used to throw me up in the air, and tell me stories, including the facts of life, which embarrassed me more than him. We were all warned by my mother not to stop this romance flourishing, not that we needed such advice. Phoebe was away at convalescent home when he entered the family; we all told her so much about him, and when she came home she wasn't disappointed. He shook hands with her the first time they met, flashed her a secretive glance, and when he left she found a sixpence in her palm. She never got over that, and was hooked like the rest of us.

However, gods have to tumble, and Ivor was no exception, though then I didn't know why he had tumbled in my mind. He would come and sit on the settee, and I would encourage him to sit back and make himself comfortable — a practice I was following with almost every visitor now — for in this way I hoped he would drop some coppers or even sixpence down the back of it. And after he'd gone, and when nobody was in the room, I'd turn the settee upside down to get the money out. I ruined the furniture that way but I just had to go to the pictures, for the world of Gary Cooper, *Marco Polo*, of *The Mark of Zorro* and *Sanders of the River*, was calling me.

Somehow now I always managed to go to the pictures every day. I'd go round to all my aunts and ask them for old clothes and rags. They, I suppose, thought I needed them for the family. Then I'd get jam jars and take them to the rag shop. And every time someone came to the house I'd ask them to lend me a farthing. By hook or by crook I'd manage it. I remember my mother saying, "Whatever that boy wants, he gets. You'll see bit by bit, whatever he wants he'll get."

I began to draw distant from the family, the house, and the games, and the playground had much less hold on me. I wanted to be on my own. One day my father punished me for being cheeky, and in his usual extreme tantrum he kicked me, though he kicked the air more. I ran out of the house and crept back in when no-one was looking and hid behind the sideboard. Hours passed, and I heard my mother crying, and I was so pleased that I, alone, could have this effect on someone.

"If only he'd come home!" she said to the others.

Well, I thought magnanimously, she's had enough punishment, so I came out — and she sloshed me round the room.

I became more aware of London, and of England. Instead of the cinema I would walk around the riverside, or get a sixpenny all-day ticket on the trams, and I'd travel past the Elephant and Castle, and sometimes even as far as New Cross or Greenwich. How beautiful Greenwich was! I could hardly believe it, and I'd stay away all day. My greatest delight was sitting upstairs on a tram, right in the front, seeing the silver lines in front of me, shooting along in the middle of the road, pretending that I was driving.

Certain things scared me on the way back to my home: for instance, I'd hate to go near a church, perhaps because my mother would always rush by if I was with her. But on my own I was even more scared, thinking that the grey sickly mass of stone would fall on top of me. This was my greatest fear as a child. And nuns were too — though this fear was shared with other Jewish children, who often saw their parents spitting seven times through their held-up fingers. I hated to see a crucifix outside a church. Why did they have a statue of a dead man outside a church? The agony and the ugliness made me close my eyes until I had passed.

Each time I would return to my house, to a terrible telling-off and a cuddle. I was getting a reputation in the family, for being a wanderer — I didn't mind at all. It seemed to make kosher the way I wanted to go, although I was completely unaware of my journey and my destination.

Some of my relatives came from Holland for the first time, and there was great excitement in the family. A great favourite of mine was a cousin, who was then quite a famous dance band leader over there. Joe Kops and his Hot Shots. He gave me something that I was hungry for: some details about the past. My family had not always been clickers and bookmakers; there were some artists in the family, and one of my uncles had been one of the most famous socialist poets some years before. This was the first time I had heard the word 'socialist' mentioned.

He told the family that we were crazy to stay in England, that we should all pack up and go back to Amsterdam, for it looked like war was coming, and Holland would be neutral. Through him I was able to find that some of my family had come from Eastern Europe, and some had come from Spain and Portugal.

Fate is a weird bitch — for my father, who came here to escape poverty, also escaped the gas chambers; and those who were well off, and stayed in Amsterdam, perished in Auschwitz.

'War.' That word kept creeping more and more into talk. But "Uncle" Leo, cousin Joe's friend, assured us that everything was going to be all right. He was a non-Jew from Germany, and he told us that Hitler's measures were temporary ones. My sisters didn't like him very much; one day I saw him touching Phoebe on her breast, and when she got angry I also took a dislike to him. We learned later that on returning to Germany he joined the Nazi party, and I believe he did quite well in the organisation.

Anyway, my father decided that England was his home. Besides, the girls were working, and we were just managing. Essie and Marie were now going to dances. One evening I remember them trying on their blue and yellow dresses that they had just made. It was such a big event in their lives and the rest of the family leaned over the balcony to watch them walk along Stepney Green proudly showing off their gowns.

Phoebe earned six shillings a week as a felling hand — and one day I went to her factory, where hundreds of girls were slaving away in a hall crammed with sewing machines. Here the clothes for Savile Row and Regent Street were being made, where rats and mice scampered along the rafters, where the girls couldn't walk past the boss without getting their behinds pinched, where my sisters were continuously being offered silk underwear by the boss, for you-know-what. My sisters never accepted, but some girls did — and it wasn't only the silk underwear, but also the flattery of being wanted by the boss. The language those girls used certainly made a ten-year-old blush. They worked from eight till six, slaving away in those places, definitively called sweatshops. And how many times my sisters would come home crying, for either the boss was trying to get fresh with them, or a needle had gone right through their finger. I wanted to know what getting fresh meant, "Don't ask too many questions," my mother said. In those days I never stopped asking questions.

If my sisters came home from work more than five minutes late, my mother was already tearing her white hair with anguish, and sending one of us to look for them, "But be careful — don't talk to no-one!"

Once I was sent to meet Phoebe in the fog, and a woman came up to us; we both screamed so much that half the street came out. The poor woman was only asking the way.

Tall stories abounded in Stepney, stories of children being burnt instead of the guy on Guy Fawkes Night; or the child that had swallowed an octopus egg, which had grown inside her until it killed her. This was the spawning ground of the underprivileged, of the boys with the gift of the gab, who had no knowledge of their roots, who dreamed of fame because fame brought money and money bought escape. We wanted to prove something to ourselves, to run twice as fast as the Christian world in order to keep up with it. I became aware of the Christian world, one terrifying day, when Eddie Cantor, the fabulous Jewish boy, the star of our dreams came to a restaurant in Whitechapel Road. Thousands of people came to cheer him.

"Bloody Jew-boy!" I heard a woman next to me mutter to herself.

She was talking about the star of *Whoopee* and *Roman Scandals* — and I pulled her coat. "But that's Eddie Cantor!" I said.

"Shut your yap, you little yid!" said a little woman, with threadbare clothes. I didn't hate her — I was just afraid. A little later I was standing outside the Troxy, the fabulous and 'biggest cinema in the world'. We were waiting to see Sophie Tucker come out, and when she came, men started to throw stones at her, and we all screamed and rushed home.

"They were lousy Blackshirts," my father said. "It's all because she sang 'Yiddisher Momma'," my mother added.

And in Itchy Park, and in Victoria Park, we weren't all playing together anymore. A group of little boys screamed at us, "The Yids! The Yids! We've got to get rid of the Yids!" I recognised a young mate amongst them, I waved, and he waved back.

So now we had slanging matches. For they would sing, 'Archibald, the King of the Jews, bought his wife a pair of shoes, when the shoes began to wear, Archibald began to swear.' We all took that as a colossal insult, and I don't know why. I mean, buying your wife a pair of shoes is a perfectly normal thing to do. Anyway, we yelled back: 'Archibald, King of the Yoks, bought his wife a pair of socks — when the socks began to wear, Archibald began to swear.' The only difference between us, it seems, was between shoes and socks.

But the Jubilee came, to take our mind off things. The Jubilee of King George V and his wife. I stood in Mile End Road with the kids from the school waving a Union Jack. The white-faced queen waved her fingers back at us, and I remember thinking, she's really dead. They've just stuffed her and put clockwork inside her. The king also. That was that. From that moment on the king and queen were made of clockwork. And all those people who I heard screaming against royalty, the tailors and the pressers and the felling hands, many calling themselves red-hot communists — they were all there with their Seebackroscopes, wildly waving Union Jacks at the passing parade.

But my dad was having none of that. "Think of all them rooms in Buckingham Palace. Empty while people are starving!" For the life of me I couldn't see how people could eat rooms. But I was now a little closer to my father. Everyone would take the rise out of him for liking classical music, because the rage in those days was the Tango, Roy Fox, Geraldo, Joe Loss and Billy Cotton. We used to fight over the wireless, but Radio Luxembourg usually won. But to stake my difference, and my independence of dance music, I decided to go with my father to see an opera, much to his surprise. So I saw my first theatrical performance *Aida*, done at the York Hall Swimming Baths. Even though I fell asleep, the sheer experience of sitting amongst dressed-up people was magnificent. I loved the entombment scene but when everybody else started crying, I couldn't understand why, and I sat forward, laughing, with the sheer delight of it all.

So I started going with him, once even to the Sadlers Wells in Islington, where we queued for three hours and didn't get in. *Faust* was my favourite of all, and Mephistopheles was the hero, whom I couldn't bear to look at.

Infant school was over, and I started going to a Christian school at the other end of Stepney Green. I used to pass a blacksmith on the way, and I was nearly always late, being intrigued by the horseshoes being made red hot, and seeing them sizzle on the horse's hooves. I loved the smell. My sister hated it.

At that school I had to learn to defend myself the hard way. I hated every teacher. Figures and numbers and words were pushed into my ears, and poems were pulverised and shoved down my throat. Once we read *The Tempest* — not bad, I remember telling a friend, but I cried when I read *The Forsaken Merman*.

One morning at prayers we were singing "All things bright and beautiful, all creatures great and small", and the boy behind me shouted out, "Kops has got a bug crawling up his coat!" That hall could have opened up to swallow me, I was so ashamed. I used to inspect my clothing every morning before I left my house, but there was always one that seemed to elude the search. And the other horror were the nits and the woppers we found in our hair even though we constantly went through it with a tooth-comb, we never seemed to get rid of them. Yet it was quite a thrill finding them, and squashing them between two thumbnails. Mind you, the black day of the soul was when the nurse came to inspect us in class. She'd sit in the front on her chair, and we'd line up, and one by one tremble under her scrutiny. More than once I had to go to the cleansing station, and on one occasion I was jeered at by some boys in the playground, boys who had also been to the same place at other times. One hit me on the nose. "Dirty git! You killed our Lord!" Through my tears I cried, "I never killed no one!"

"I mean Jesus!"

"That was a long time ago — and I didn't have nothing to do with it." In those days I always thought that Christ had been a traitor, the Yiddisher boy who fell amongst *goyim*. Anyway, I fought over it, and later got rapped on the bum by a master for making a lot of noise.

My mother came up to the school. She always did on these occasions, and I heard her as I was sitting in the class, and then I'd see her burst into the classroom, five feet tall and four feet across, shouting, "Where's that master who hit my boy? I want to see the headmaster!" She always came up to school, even though we always tried to keep it from her or beg her not to come, and even though she promised she wouldn't, she always did.

Later, discussing Christ and *schicksers* and *goys*, my father told me there were two sorts of people in the world: Jews and Jew-haters. And as a Jew I had to hate the haters.

Now the fights began in earnest, especially when I went to the penny pictures with my brother in the Commercial Road, a place designed to keep us out of mischief and off the streets — but the mischief that went on in that Mission Hall, no tongue can tell. The fights before the show began, in the aisle, between the Jews and the Christians and Mr Walker, the cripple with his dog-collar, innocently preaching brotherly love, before the Flash Gordon serial. Or those horrors about the destruction of the Red Indian, when our fights were forgotten, and the world was divided simply between good 'uns and bad 'uns. And like the rest of the audience I jumped up and down with delight whenever an Indian fell off his horse.

The name Hitler crept more and more into the conversation at home. Now I knew he was definitely not in the family, but was out to get every one of us. And every Sunday morning a new show was being enacted in Stepney Green, a frightening horrible show run by a man called Mosley, who looked like a Jew, who some said was even partly Jewish. That explained it. "Explained what?" I asked. Grown-ups were too busy to answer a boy who asked too many questions; but events gave me the answer.

The first person to get a pitch in Stepney Green held the meeting on Sunday morning. The Communists and Blackshirts and Blue and White Shirts used to try to outdo each other by arriving earliest, until in the end they began to arrive late Saturday night. My mother would lie awake, staring out of the window, to see who got the pitch. If it was the Blue and White Shirts, or the Communists, she'd go to sleep relieved. But if it was the Blackshirts she'd stay awake all night, and there was a terrible tension Sunday morning. But mostly on Sunday morning, those men in their shiny black uniforms, with their great black vans and loudspeakers, would hold the meeting. I knew they must have very rich friends because who else could afford uniforms in those days? Especially some of those men whom I recognised from the Labour Exchange, or Duckett Street, who used to wear rags. The lightning flash was the dreaded symbol, especially since I was afraid of lightning.

Then the big boss would arrive, and the whole of Stepney Green was black with people, Sir Oswald Mosley would try to speak.

But we had not been idle in the early morning, and had been going from door to door to collect pennies. Then we'd rush to buy whistles and blowers, and collect saucepan lids, and we'd stand on the landings banging the lids and the kettles and the saucepans together. The police could do nothing about it because we were on private property. Mosley wanted the publicity — he came into the heart of the Jewish area to provoke us. But we certainly stopped him speaking in Stepney Green by kicking up the most hellish noise.

Sometimes I ventured into the street, and I saw the policemen on their horses, protecting the Blackshirts, and swinging wildly at the people I knew. I saw my own brother, an onlooker, hit over the head with a truncheon, and he fell to the ground. But one of my big cousins saw it also. A few weeks later he and his three brothers waited in a doorway in Jubilee Street, and when the policeman passed they did him up good and proper. They had remembered his number, and shadowed him.

We in the East End had no doubt that the police were loaded against us. So you see I grew up with a healthy hatred for the law, a hatred and a knowledge that has given me a wonderful sense of security, and placed me in a good position for the rest of my life. After all, it's good to know where you stand, it's good to know who are the enemy. And it's excellent, at an early age, to differentiate between the police force and justice.

Everyone seemed to be wearing shirts in those days. They'd swing through with their bands playing, the Greenshirts, the Orangeshirts, the Blackshirts and the Blue and White Shirts. I joined the junior Blue and White Shirts, and though I didn't know what they stood for, I knew that they stood against fascism. I used to run messages for them, usually given to me by a man called Mr Pritchard, who later got killed in Spain. The balloon was going up in Stepney — there were people out to get us, and we didn't wander the streets so freely any more. Mothers called their children home earlier.

The climax came one day when I was passing Aldgate with my father. There were barricades, and thousands of mounted police.

"What's happening?" I asked.

"The Blackshirts are trying to march through," he replied. From my small height I could see marbles being thrown under the hooves of the horses, and horses going over, and I could hear people screaming and shouting, and the terrible urgency of fire engines and ambulances.

"They shall not pass! Mosley shall not pass!"

"The Yids! The Yids! We've got to get rid of the Yids!"

"They shall not pass! They shall not pass!" Over and over again. And they did not pass. That was the beginning of the end of Sir Oswald Mosley and his under-privileged boys.

"But who stopped them? Who stopped them?" I kept asking my father on the way home.

"The dockers did," he replied proudly. "It was the dockers."

I had seen many dockers on my walks, past St George's Docks and East India Docks.

"But dockers aren't Jewish, dad, are they? I mean, Jews are tailors and furriers, aren't they?"

My father agreed.

"But I thought you said the world was divided between Jews and Jew-haters?"

I asked the question twice, and he seemed confused, I felt

sorry for him — and very, very pleased with myself. Not for my question, but because of the events of that day. We hurried back to my home, and we all had supper.

* * *

So, They're Also Human

Suddenly everybody started reading newspapers. The Zetters, my racing cousins, always did read the back page but suddenly the Kopses started reading the front page. This was ominous. The headlines got bigger and bigger and blacker and blacker. You didn't need to be a prophet to know which way the wind was blowing.

My father flung down the *Daily Mail* and stamped on it, "Look, they'd welcome that bastard Hitler." My mother, shaking her head between her hands, said, "So, they're also human, it'll all blow over." And my racing cousins added to my mother's optimism, "Bet you half a nicker nothing will come of it." Anything for a bet. If the world was coming to an end they would be betting each other on the exact time of day.

It got dark very early one particular day and my young sister Rose followed my mother around the house constantly clutching at her dress. "She's driving me mad," my mother said.

It poured with rain and all the children looked like doom and Rose became hysterical, screaming that the rain would drown everybody in the world.

I just had to get out of the house. So, taking advantage of her anxiety, I asked my mother for sixpence. She gave it to me without knowing what she was doing. "They're all driving me mad," I could hear her repeating as I ran down the stairs.

There I was, eleven years old, striding up Stepney Green, saying to myself, "All right, even if the earth is going to get blown to pieces, that isn't the end of the world."

Near the top of Stepney Green I, met Mr Green, "Where you off to?"

"Dunno, for a ride. Is there going to be a war?"

"Without a shadow of doubt, I can feel it in my water. I'm never wrong." He spoke as though he had lived through a thousand wars. And he had in a way, with his wife. Mind you I liked her more than him.

"So, they're also human." My mother's words echoed through my head as I sat on the 25 bus. "They've also got children." The bus raced towards the West End. I wanted to believe my mother but I knew her too well. If we were all on a raft starving, surrounded by sharks she'd probably say "Thank God we've got our health and strength". How often had I fallen down, grazed my knees and cut my forehead, sprained a finger and she'd rub the afflicted part and say, "Good, good, you might have broken your legs."

But this was my first journey Up West and I was much too excited to worry about the world situation any more. Head averted, eyes staring wide, I stood in the marble palace of Lyons Corner House and heard a few strains of the Gypsy band. Then it occurred to me that probably my mother had never been to the West End in all her life. People looked so happy. I wandered round the streets — drawn to the bright lights of the windows, banging my head against the glass windows, like a moth, pressing my nose close to the confectionery shops.

And there was one shop in particular behind Tottenham Court Road. It had a Jewish sounding name. It was full of sausages and fat people eating, dressed in beautiful clothes. I pressed my face against that window too, my mouth watering. Then I got the most terrible fright. On the wall was a photograph of Hitler, a Union Jack and a swastika on either side. I was terrified, afraid that they would pull me inside and kill me and I rushed home in panic. That's how they make their sausages.

"So, they're also human," my mother repeated, trying to allay my fears. But from that moment on, I knew for certain that the war was coming.

This statement "So, they're also human" was one my mother applied to any people who were not Jewish. For instance, one day a boy I knew got knocked over by a car. I told my mother later.

"Yiddisher boy?" she enquired.

"No," I replied, "he's a Christian."

"So, they're also human." A terrible attitude yet, in a way, understandable in a tightknit community where universal truths could only be expressed through the specific. Besides, Jewish people didn't only have this attitude to non-Jews. They ridiculed Jews from other communities, denigrated each other mercilessly. Humorously, perhaps, but nevertheless denigration.

My father would often say, "What can you expect of a Polak," or "Lousy Germans". And the Polaks would say, "What can you expect from a Litvak" or "Bloody Chutz". My father's worst insult to a fellow Jew was, "He's a lousy Peruvian", God knows why this was an insult, and what was a Peruvian anyway? Surely someone who came from Peru. Not to my father. The Jews from Holland, they were wonderful; the Spanish Jews? At least they were reserved. But all the others? You could keep them. Even the Bulgarian Yidden. But it was the Peruvians, the unclassified Jews who made him go really red in the face.

How often the woman next door said in her thickest Russian Yiddish, "The trouble with this country is there are too many bloody foreigners."

But joking, like the broken glass, can't hold up the weather. People may have been smiling and stuffing themselves in the West End but in Eastern Europe states were being carved up and now letters were arriving constantly from Holland imploring us to leave England and go there.

My mother's health got worse and she coughed most of the time. How I hated her coughing. The more she gasped for breath the more I wanted to get away. And I did. But in a way that I didn't expect. For months I had been having terrible pains in my body. So much so, that the world situation became a rather second-rate fear. Believe me, I had troubles enough of my own.

I was afraid to tell my mother in case she would take me to the hospital and they would tell her that I was going to die. Or they might keep me in. To be 'kept in hospital' was a terrible phrase in the East End. For when children were *schlapped* away from their parents and taken up to the wards, it was a major tragedy for both parent and child, no matter how minor the illness was. No subtle psychological softening-up processes. Anyway, the pain started attacking my fingers and legs. One day she saw the pain from my expression.

"What's the matter, what's the matter?" She was always like that, eagle-eyed in anticipation of appendicitis or a sore throat. Anyway, it all came out. It always did in the end. You can't hide anything in a Jewish family. I was rushed to the hospital there and then, even though I had been walking around with it for two months.

It was nothing romantic or dramatic like a sudden operation needed for peritonitis, or too much blood or not enough. It was merely severe rheumatism. Not even anything to do with my earlier illness of rickets which, despite its name, had a certain distinction. But I had to be kept in, nevertheless, and despite my tears a great part of me enjoyed the drama. Or at least part of me was outside, watching myself crying as I was torn away from my mother's skirt. The nurse reassured me there was nothing to worry about. So did my mother, tears rolling down her face as she did so.

For a few days I was kept at the London Jewish Hospital, building castles with cards, and happy with the men and sinking down in my bed with a white face at visiting times. And my locker filling with chocolates and oranges but never flowers. Jewish people rarely used to take flowers when they visited an invalid. After all you can't eat flowers, and they die so quickly. Besides, flowers have a kind of personality and four visitors around the bed all competing for attention cannot afford such a colourful rival.

I fell for a nurse. A white-gowned probationer.

"Angels of mercy," my mother said. "They're all Yiddisher girls too." We were all so proud that everything in the Jewish Hospital was Jewish, even the X-ray machines. *Goyim* also used to come to that hospital for treatment. It gave me a wonderful sense of satisfaction to see Christians in the out-patients. Maybe they won't hate us so much, I thought.

In the London Jewish Hospital they were very kind and it was a blow to hear that I was being moved to a special children's hospital, somewhere in the country.

"The country?" my mother said. "What's wrong with London, why do they have to move him miles away? What's so good in the country?" I, who needed soothing, tried to soothe her. This soothed me, besides, the thought of leaving Stepney Green excited me. "But it's not a Yiddisher hospital," my mother said.

A fat lot I cared. A hospital is a hospital, with nurses always waking you up at five in the morning to give you a blanket bath and pour horrible medicine down your throat. And the smell of disinfectant and polish and someone always moaning in the night. So I was moved.

As soon as I saw the building I knew I was going to hate it. I started to retch. I don't know why. And though the hospital was surrounded by trees I felt very afraid. It seemed endless, to go on

38

and on for ever. As the ambulance men carried me into the ward something died within me. A part of my life was over and all excitement left me. I was terribly alone. They could come and visit me twice a week but I was on my own, away from the world of Stepney Green.

My bed was on a balcony. An open balcony attached to the ward. A strange place I would have thought for a child suffering from rheumatism. "Still, they know best," I tried comforting myself with the comfortable language of grown-ups. My first day was made bearable by the boy in the next bed who suddenly used the longest word I had ever heard. "Contradiction." "What a beautiful word," I thought as I repeated it syllable by syllable.

The food was terrible. And then, of all things, when the night threatened all the children started to sing a hymn.

"Now the day is over and night is drawing nigh, shadows of the evening steal across the sky." It made me feel sick. I was so lonely and cold I cried myself to sleep.

I woke in the night. Everyone was asleep and everything was dark except for the blue light of the night nurse, and the branches of the trees were tearing at the moon. For the first time in my life I was really afraid; not even Mosley or the Police had made me feel so low — willingly I would have walked out of that hospital and got back to Stepney Green somehow. I thought about it, saw myself on the main road in my pyjamas. But you know how it is, you never do under these circumstances.

Within a few days it became like a prison to me. I felt I was in there for some sort of punishment.

I asked the boy in the next bed if he knew what was happening in the world, if he had any idea what the latest news was. He looked at me as if I was mad. I didn't want to ask the nurse in case she told me the worst. But then what was world war compared to the night nurse who was a rotten old bitch who looked like a witch? And that was her nickname — Witch.

Away from the family for the first time the wind was taken right out of my sails. I started wetting the bed regularly. The shame of it. The night nurse in the morning would hold up the sheet for the children to see and they would laugh, but not the kid in the next bed. But the more they ridiculed me the more I wet the bed.

"We'll have to give you a rubber sheet, like a baby of two," the night nurse said. And they did. "Angels of Mercy?" Bitterness entered my life.

I tried everything I knew to stop wetting that bed. Almost stopped drinking but that didn't work. The puddles and the patches on the sheet got larger. Stark fear overcame me. I even considered tying up my penis with string. Then I tried keeping awake all night. I once managed to keep awake until dawn but then I fell asleep between four and six and when I awoke I was soaked in urine. The other children wouldn't talk to me; even though some of them wet the bed. I was older, was expected to know better. My whole life centred around this. When my parents came to visit me I must have looked twice as bad as when I was admitted. I refused to tell them what was wrong.

At nights now I tried other tactics. In secret, when everyone else was asleep, I would strip the sheets off the bed and lay on the rubber and when that didn't work I tried to move the mattress slightly to one side and lay on the spring. Then in the morning early I would mop up with my pyjama jacket. But then there was the problem of what to do with the pyjama jacket. Anyway the spring was cutting too much into my body so I again lay on the sheets. One night, having got water from the nurse for supposed thirst, I tried to wash the sheet out and hang it over the balcony. She caught me and smacked me. If I wet on the mattress I would turn it over while all the others slept. But I was always discovered by the morning nurses making the beds. It was no joke, they rubbed my nose in it.

The climax to my nightmare came one lunch time. Eating my lunch I found I couldn't swallow the cabbage stalks or the gluey tapioca. By now the nurses couldn't stand me and one of them forced it all down my throat and when I was sick they made me eat my sick.

"The Yiddified bastards," my mother said. And I think she wanted to take me home, but there was a sort of mystical attitude towards the hospital. After all, they were trying to get me better. I screamed when she left. But a few days later when my sister Phoebe came to visit me I was very quiet. I didn't need to say anything. She went straight home and told my mother that they had to get me out immediately. And they did. They came with my clothes there and then and I dressed and sang the song I had learned there:

40

I'm off to London next Sunday morning.
I'm off to London half past eight.
Give my love to the dear old doctor,
Tell him I can't stay here any longer.

Only I didn't give my love to the dear old doctor and my mother and Phoebe swept me out of the hospital gates and on to a Green Line coach, back to the East End.

"The *momsers*," my mother said angrily. But I wasn't angry because I was so happy and so grateful to Phoebe, whom I have loved dearly ever since.

I must have looked very, very ill when I returned home, because they all just stared at me and quickly upholstered smiles. They spoiled me for over a week, It was wonderful.

In a Jewish household nothing heals quicker than sadness — they simply wouldn't let me be withdrawn. Besides there was also the compensation of Munich. Though looking back, some compensation.

The woman next door came running in with a newspaper. It sounded as if she was shouting, "Piss in our time," I wondered what on earth she was talking about.

The house became crowded with relatives and friends. Oh, I loved the look of Mr Chamberlain. My mother said, "I knew it, God is good."

Rumours were flying thick and fast. "Somebody said he's partly a Yiddisher feller," someone said. Anybody we revered had Jewish blood somewhere. But the *Jewish Chronicle* hadn't claimed him so he couldn't have been, but my brother fingered his photograph in the newspaper. "He's got a moustache just like dad."

"So's Hitler," I chimed in.

"Is it good for the Yiddisher people?" my Aunt Betsie asked. "Of course it is," Mr Lever replied.

"What about the Yids in Czechoslovakia?" my father asked. "Anyway if there's war there'll be plenty of work." Nobody replied to him. "God is good," my mother repeated.

"It had nothing to do with God," said Mr Zuman who surprisingly came out of his almost trappist vow of silence. Up to then all I had ever heard him say was to sigh every half-hour, "*Oy vayz meer.*"

But we pored over the newspapers and savoured every word.

41

Suddenly even Hitler looked nice. The Jeremiah from next door said, "Didn't I tell you all along everything would be all right? I study these things."

But my mother wondered what it meant, "peace in our time". Did it mean war some other time? How long is "our time"?

Adults may have been taken in, but I don't think the children were. After all, a few weeks later they started practising with barrage balloons and searchlights in the sky. And there was talk of us all getting gas masks. A strange prelude to peace.

A letter came telling that I was being sent convalescent to Hove.

"It's a Yiddisher convalescent home, so you'll be all right there," my mother said. Besides, the Jewish Board of Guardians had arranged it, This title had always summoned up a picture of kind old Jewish gentlemen with long beards.

So I saw the sea for the first time and this time they were kind to me. And even though the bed-wetting continued no-one ever mentioned it. I think it cleared up soon after that.

It was the first time I had been thrown together with religious Jews and, though I couldn't read or take to the prayers I mumbled gibberish and they all thought I could pray. The fried fish was out of this world. It was almost worth being ill to have such fried fish. I wrote home about it.

The sea fascinated but frightened me, for I remembered the warnings of my mother. "Take care you only paddle, and only up to the ankles." And when I did paddle I always faced the beach and never looked out to sea.

Brighton beach was crowded and I strolled in the sun, and though I envied the kids of holiday-makers noshing ice-cream, it was still paradise. One day I saw Lobby Lud. He was the man from the *News Chronicle*. You had to present him with the *News Chronicle* and say exactly, "You are Mr Lobby Lud and I claim the *News Chronicle* prize." I chased him but I didn't catch him. Anyway, I never had a *News Chronicle*.

On the beach, the *Daily Mirror Eight* were exercising. Lovely girls dressed all in white, moving rhythmically to music, surrounded by thousands of people.

My mother had warned me also not to go into the water too often because of my rheumatism, implored me always to dress up warm and do up my neck.

Every opportunity I got I was paddling in the water in an

open-necked shirt, and after several weeks I felt marvellous. But paradise became boring and I was homesick again and wasn't sorry to be discharged and to return to Stepney Green.

Besides, there were weddings soon. Meanwhile, I returned to my dreary school, where Mr Swaffer suddenly announced that we were going to study algebra. I was bad enough at almost everything, but at algebra I was catastrophic. Everyone in the class seemed to understand what he was talking about and I could add up and take away with the best of them, or the worst of them, but algebra was completely beyond me.

To add insult to ignominy the algebra teacher was also the sports master. I think I stood a better chance of living in Park Lane than kicking a football, even if the ball was right in front of my foot. Anyway, one day at cricket I was wicketkeeper, and slightly proud of my position. The batsman missed the ball, the ball hit me on the nose and the bat hit me in the temple. The playground seemed to coagulate around me — mild concussion.

When I returned to school we sat for exams and everybody asked everybody else what they would do in a year's time when they finished school. I didn't have the slightest idea. Most of the others were very sure of themselves.

Essie got married and my mother cried for joy. Jewish mothers always cry for something. Ivor paid for the wedding and my father never stopped telling everyone about it. We celebrated on the seventh flight of Stepney Green Buildings. Two houses were thrown wide open and tables were put together to make one long table going from the bedroom of our house over the landing and into the bedroom of the neighbour's house. There were several sittings to dinner and did we *fress*? Ivor was once more resurrected in my imagination. He had a way of winning hearts with a wink. All the neighbours stood around as we sat eating and talking and singing and jabbering, and eating and drinking and talking.

"What do you think of it eh?" my father kept saying. "He's very well off."

"I'm the luckiest woman in the world," my sister said to my other sister.

"My daughters have really done well for themselves. And why shouldn't they, they're good girls," my mother told Aunt Liddy.

Essie and Ivor got a little flat in Bow and she stopped going to work. He gave her a shilling a day for lunch and she came to our

43

house to eat with us. I would meet her along the Green, grab the coin, dash to get potatoes and eggs, and out of her shilling all of us would have egg and chips for lunch.

I remember how my father moaned around that time. "Just when they grow up and earn a bit of cash they get married and leave you."

By now my parents were hypnotising me into my future work. Either I had to go into the same thing as my father or become a chef. I couldn't argue with them because it all didn't mean very much to me. I wasn't ambitious but my father was always saying, "A poor Yiddisher boy can't afford to be ambitious". I wondered what 'ambitious' meant. He put the word into my head. So I enquired and found out what it meant.

This attitude of my father's wasn't typical. Rather incredible when you consider how he suffered in the leather factories. Still, he did say I could become a chef and this did appeal to me. Maybe it was the thought of having lovely food and those white hats made you look so tall. No-one knew how you set about becoming a chef, and nobody enquired.

By now everybody except Rose and myself were working but we were still badly off. All the money was spent on food, for we were seven growing children with insatiable stomachs.

My brothers were flexing their muscles, becoming more proud and particular, and Jack even bought a new suit. I used to look at it with love and envy and brush the lapels with my fingers, especially when I was taking it to the pawn shop. And now I was going there alone because the stairs were getting too much for my mother. The suit was being pawned without Jack's knowledge. He'd wear it on a weekend and I'd pawn it on Monday, then on Friday evening, when he brought his wages home, my mother would divert him, engage him in conversation while she'd slip me some money. I'd rush to the pawn shop, bring the suit back and get it into his room somehow without him seeing. It always worked smoothly except once, and then it was murder. But the suit continued to be pawned.

Marie got married. She was my oldest sister and we were all relieved, because she was no little Mae West like Essie, but rather homely and serious. Her boyfriend, Mick, the complete opposite to Ivor, was quiet and small and muttered few words. Born in Kiev, he came from 'a good family'. His parents had a grocery shop. This impressed us very much and on top of that he had a good trade. A cabinet-maker; he was making a good living.

The wedding was held at the Grand Palais in Commercial Road where the Yiddish Theatre used to be housed. Those actors who overacted magnificently would have been hard put to have equalled the performance of my assembled family that evening. And there was a band also, playing right through dinner. For weeks before I boasted to everyone there was going to be an orchestra. Well, all right, three musicians can be called an orchestra. Anyway I called it one.

Mick's family paid for the wedding, and my mother cried her usual tears of joy. "What do you think of it? His family paid for everything." The only dowry he inherited was the Kops family.

What a dinner! Dave, Phoebe and myself put chicken legs into our pockets. Not because we couldn't cope, but because we were thinking of tomorrow. And my father wore a top hat. He was drunk, laughing and singing.

"I feel like a millionaire," he said, puffing a disintegrating cigar, ash smeared all down his lapels. We all stood around him, pointing and laughing, and he danced with us. And Ivor did the *Chuzutska* and the young cousins joined in. I realised then that the veneer of England and Europe was very thin upon us. "*Oy-yoy shiker is a goy.*" We sang and danced until we collapsed and then we got up again and ate ice-cream until we burst and then we ate some more.

The older men played cards, serious and quiet, oblivious to everything under a cloud of cigar smoke. The children were running around and playing, the old women were *yachnering*, the young girls giggling and the young men feeling each other's cloth and comparing their new ties.

Dave and I were so proud showing off our new suits, the first new suits we ever had. With long trousers and Eton collars.

The wedding finished at two o'clock in the morning and Mick got a taxi to take us home. My first taxi ride, and I enjoyed that even more than the wedding. All of us singing through the night streets of the East End. "*Bei mir bis du schein — on Hitler's broch on der brain,*" But as we wound up the stairs to the top, my mother tried to shut us up in case we woke the neighbours.

Came the dawn and the reckoning. Each of us nibbling the remains of our chicken legs and stuffing ourselves with liquorice allsorts. I wanted to keep my suit on all day but my mother wouldn't let me. I saw her brushing it on the table. I knew why.

"Please don't pawn it," I begged.

"I'm not making no promises." She sighed and I cried. But she pawned the suits later in the day. Well, you can't eat cloth, I argued philosophically with myself. But I implored her time and again, "Please don't leave it there. Get it out soon." She promised.

And she meant to, but we never saw those suits again. I thought about that lost suit so often in my life.

Peace in our time was a beautiful but empty expression, "I told you so," one of my betting cousins said. I didn't remind him that he never stopped saying that there'd never be a war ever again. The talk of war started again as Hitler started to move. This was it. And I, looking over Stepney Green, felt unsafe, so vulnerable, watching the barrage balloons hanging low in the sky.

'Where can I run?" I thought. "Where can I hide?" I knew there was nowhere.

At school, much to my surprise, I had done well in the exam. The boys and the teacher couldn't believe the results. Neither could I. But I had won a scholarship. I thought there must have been some mistake but I wasn't going to question it, because in the hall, before the assembled school, the headmaster announced the result and told us we were all getting a half-day holiday because of my, and a few others, endeavours.

"Good old Kopsy."

I had put down to go to a catering school, so it looked as if I was going to get my tall white hat after all.

But Hitler had other ideas.

And any celebration in the family on my behalf was lost in the terrible news and the certainty of the coming war and the fact that we were to be evacuated.

My mother said, "Just when things start going well for us, that *momser* has to spoil everything."

All children of school age were to be moved from London. That meant just Rose and me alone out of the family. We kept it from Rose until the last moment.

"But we're all going to get killed," she cried. My mother's optimism had subsided, yet still she clung to a strand. "Even if there is a war, they won't bomb innocent people. They're also human."

"I want to stay with you. I want to get killed with you," Rose screamed as we assembled in the playground with our gas masks and labels tied to our coats. And then we all moved away, all the children and all the parents crying. And again, for me the fear and the excitement, I know that for my mother the separation from us was even worse than the thought of war.

We marched away in crocodile fashion and I looked back at Stepney Green. The leaves so green in the September sunlight. This was the place where we were born, where we grew up, where we played and sang, laughed and cried. And now all the grey faces as we passed were weeping. It was strangely quiet. Only the birds in the trees were singing now. They didn't know about the crisis. They didn't know what man was bringing to the earth.

In the train I could hardly contain myself with excitement when it moved out of the station, I jumped from window to window. But then I came back to earth with a clunk when I looked at my terrible responsibility, my crying snotty-nosed red-eyed little sister. I had promised to look after her and not to be separated from her.

"But where will we be tonight?" she appealed to me. And I shrugged, "Your guess is as good as mine."

"But we'll be with strangers." Rose had never been away from home, never been more than six inches away from my mother and now she was clinging on to me and the other children were watching us. "Will we be with Christians?"

I reassured her, "So, they're also human."

* * *

I Hear Sirens

"Stand out all the boys who can't swim," the games master said, and three or four of us stood on the edge of the swimming pool. He said he was going to teach us how and gave us a sharp shove into the water. It was only the shallow end but I slipped and my head got covered. I struggled under the water. When I came to the surface I screamed and screamed. I could hear my voice echoing through the baths and I saw all the boys staring at me, To this day I have never got over my fear of water, I even hate crossing it in a boat.

47

But I used to stare at the sea every day and became obsessed by it. The sea surrounded us and at any time she might pounce and reclaim her lost continents.

The school moved inland when the phoney war ended and I wasn't sorry. At Dorking in Surrey I was billeted on a colonel's estate with several other boys. A maid waited on us and one day asked me to touch her breasts. It was the first time I had touched full-blown breasts. They were beautiful. Whenever she referred to sex and having babies she called her womb her wound.

I still didn't know what I wanted to be but I knew what I didn't want to be. And that was a waiter. How I hated those stiff collars. All the time I was now thinking of going back to London and throwing it all up. "How? How?" I racked my brain for an excuse to escape and my opportunity came soon enough for German planes were now crossing the coast daily. Now I was hearing sirens all the time.

That day of days, more Heinkels than usual crossed over Surrey. I crouched in the shelter with the other boys and masters and everything shook with the guns, and I shook with fright, unable to stop my teeth chattering and I was ashamed to appear afraid. There was a tremendously loud explosion and later, after the all clear, we heard that a Heinkel bomber, full of bombs, had crashed in a field about a mile away. That afternoon there was confusion and I got the urge to visit my family, so I just left the school and got a Green Line coach to London.

London looked magnificent and I got off the coach at Aldgate, stood by Petticoat Lane, walked along Whitechapel Road, whistling a favourite song and in my head recalling the words, "I went down the lane to buy a penny whistle. A copper came behind and took away my whistle. I asked him for it back, he said I haven't got it, Hi, Hi! Curly wig, you've got it in your pocket".

When I reached the Buildings I scooted up those seven flights to my home.

"What's the matter, what's the matter," my mother said, seeing me.

"Why have you left the school?" my father said, he being much more concerned with the prospects of me making a living.

I felt I had to dramatise the situation in order to stop being a waiter for the rest of my life.

"A bomber, German, full of bombs," I spoke very slowly and all the family hung on my words. "Full of bombs," I repeated, "was shot down and crashed on the school and exploded and destroyed the school. Two masters were killed and five boys, and I'm all bruised."

"Where, where?" My mother rushed towards me anxious to know the afflicted part in order to rub it.

"I'm afraid I can't show you the exact spot." That impressed them.

"You mean to say you can't go back to school again?" my Dad moaned.

"How can I if it's not there?" I replied.

"What's the matter with you Johnny? The boy's injured." My mother pulled me close and quickly poured me some soup. And from that moment on I believed that story myself. It was only years later I realised it was a complete fabrication.

When Holland was invaded, the war really hit us and my mother sobbed. For weeks we worried about the family over there. But she cheered herself up with "Maybe they won't treat them so bad". But I, who had managed to read a copy of *Mein Kampf*, lent me in secret by my cousin, was under no illusions. For there it all was, in black and white, what Hitler intended to do with all of us. I read the book in horror and fascination. Strange to think it was one of the first books I ever read. I think I gave up the family in Holland there and then but I never ever contradicted my mother, and agreed that they probably were in an internment camp.

Dunkirk! The war became more than real, became a nightmare, but these English people, people like the Thompsons, were now showing the other side of their coin and I was so grateful that I had been born in England, and Churchill's name was probably being blessed in every synagogue in the world. And in every Jewish home and Jewish heart, except, of course, those who couldn't forget the class war.

"But he's a bloody Conservative," one of my uncles said. There we were locked in the middle of a life and death struggle, and planes darting closer every day to London, and my uncle was still talking about that traitor Ramsay MacDonald and the stinking Conservative party.

The sirens went nearly every day and my mother, all sixteen stone of her, would be the first downstairs and into my Aunt Katie's house on the ground floor. She was the first one there, and I was always the second. My mother heard sirens before they even began but then she was hearing sirens all the time by now.

I remember her rushing down seven flights, her shoes falling off on the way, and she continued running in her bare feet and I was too scared to pick up the shoes. I was very ashamed of being so scared, especially on September the fifth, when I even managed to catch up with my mother and somehow overtake her. As she ran down she knocked on the window of every flat. "Air raid, air raid, air raid," as if they hadn't heard.

Down in Aunt Katie's flat, the entire Kops and Zetter families sought refuge. Every room was crammed with the dreary Kopses and the excitable Zetters. The Zetters feeling rather restless because the war had interfered with horse-racing. But now the Kopses had something to really worry about and they came into their own. Crisis and cataclysm took the place of family quarrels.

Two days before the blitz started, three bombs dropped on Stepney Green, one in the park just in front of the Buildings, smack in front of our block.

"It's always the poor who suffer," my father said. "Why don't they drop them on Park Lane?"

"Was it a bomb?" one of my dazed aunts yelled. "Well, it wasn't a firework," I replied. "We're finished! We're finished!" a girl cousin cried.

"It's the same the whole world over, it's the poor what gets the blame." My Uncle Hymie sang and made all of us laugh, but a kind of hollow laughter for we were waiting for the all-clear to see what the damage was.

When it came we realised that it was our house that had copped it. It wasn't destroyed but the blast had made it uninhabitable. We rushed upstairs to investigate but it was getting dark and we brought down a bundle each and that was that. We left everything else behind. That was the end of 23 Stepney Green Buildings. And for the next few days we all lived communally in Aunty Katie's place.

On September the seventh, the bombers came early. That day stands out like a flaming wound in my memory. Imagine a ground floor flat, crowded with hysterical women, crying babies and great crashes in the sky and the whole earth shaking. Someone rushed in, "The docks are alight. All the docks are alight." I could smell burning.

"Trust the poor to get it in the neck, why don't they sort out the rich?"

The men started to play cards and the women tried a little singsong, singing "I saw the old homestead and faces I loved" or "Don't go down in the mines dad, dreams very often come true" or "Yiddle mit'n fiddle", but every so often twenty women's fists shook at the ceiling, cursing the explosions, Germany, Hitler.

"May he die from a lingering tumour," my mother wailed. "That's too good for him," Aunt Sarah said. They sat around, those old people. About thirty of them, with a collective age of roughly one thousand and five hundred years. And on their faces was an accumulation of suffering and dread and hope and fear. Revealing the story of our people since we wandered over the face of the world.

Yes, cursing got my mother and my aunts through those early days. I sat under the table where above the men were playing cards, screwing my eyes up and covering my ears, counting the explosions.

"We're all gonna be killed, we're finished," one of my aunts became hysterical.

"Churchill will get us through, he's a friend of the Yiddisher people." With these words she was soothed.

This time all my uncles nodded agreement, even the Marxist playing solo.

The all-clear sounded a beautiful symphony in my ears, and everyone relaxed, the men arguing politics, and the women talking about food. But the younger people wandered out to see the fires and I went with them, towards the Commercial Road. The closer I got, the more black and red it became, with flames shooting higher than the cranes along the dockside. Sparks were spitting everywhere and tongues of fire consumed the great warehouses along the black and orange water of the Thames. Everything was chaos except the fire which was like a living monster with an insatiable appetite. And I was afraid of being devoured, besides I hated to watch the firemen working so hard so I left by myself and wandered back towards Stepney Green where black smoke covered the sky.

Yet, with all this, there was still a feeling of unreality. I couldn't believe it, it was like a film being shown before my eyes. Men were rushing around selling newspapers, screaming about the amount of German planes that were brought down, and there had been a family wiped out where I had just been standing. A boy from Redmans Road rushed up to me, excited, "Did yer hear about the German pilot wot was shot down. Came down by parachute and was wearing women's underclothes. People tore him to pieces." He claimed he saw it with his own eyes but I didn't believe him. I could believe the tearing to pieces part, but why should a pilot wear a woman's underclothes? That was too much to swallow.

The smoke made my eyes smart and water. A policeman standing near told me not to cry. "Don't worry sonny, we're going to beat the hell out of those Germans." His words, however, gave me no comfort. On the contrary, I couldn't cope with a kind policeman, not after my views about the law. It just gave me new problems.

When I got near the Buildings I could see my mother standing there screaming out for her children. "My children, my children? Where are my children?" She was so relieved to see me she chastised me.

"They're coming tonight. Quick! Quick!" She *schlapped* me into Aunt Katie's, where a nucleus of relatives were sitting bent round the radio listening to Lord Haw-Haw.

"Today the Jews of London are shaking in their shoes, but tonight there will be no more Jews."

I looked out of the window and watched the darkening sky. But the flames took over from the daylight and the whole world was red. The family inquest reached only one conclusion. The Germans had set fire to the docks in order to have a beacon for the coming night of terror. We knew we were in for it. "So it's the poor Jews who will have to suffer," my father said, shaking his head up and down, as Jews had done for two thousand years before him.

"God is good, we'll get over it." My mother's faith must have been lined with asbestos. But I couldn't think of getting over it and lived purely in the present, nervously talking to myself, playing the fool, or going to the lavatory several times over. When the siren wailed the bombers were on its tail.

"Tell me Mum, how you make plava cake." I wanted to engage her in conversation, not only for her sake. Besides I thought these recipes had never been written down. I was sure my mother had her own special way of cooking that had never been used by anyone else.

"Don't drive me mad."

"No seriously, how do you make it?"

"Look, you take a bit of sugar and a bit of flour and some eggs. A bit of this and a bit of that."

Above the Buildings the planes were diving and inside I was dying. And she was holding on to me to keep herself straight and to comfort me.

"What do you mean, a bit of this and that? What are the quantities?"

"How should I know? What do you want of my life?"

My uncles were cracking dirty stories in the corner, the long drawn-out dramatic episodes only punctuated by the bombs. And my mother lost herself in the crowd of aunts, who were eating nervously. The air in the room was stale with smoke. Smoke from the fires outside and the cigarettes inside.

I got a strange feeling of loneliness, of being cut off in that lighted room, cut off from all existence. Most of the kids had dropped off to sleep but I lay outstretched on the floor counting the explosions. Someone prayed.

"A fat lot of good that'll do you," a Zetter said.

How long is a night of terror? I collared my mother again, "How do you make *gefilte* fish?"

But the all-clear went and I never learnt how to make *gefilte* fish. And now I have to buy it in jars. A very third-rate substitute for that most wonderful dish of my mother's, brought about somehow by adding a little bit of this with a little bit of that and adding just a bit of this and that.

"Oh, I've got such a pain," I said to my mother.

"Go to the lavatory then."

"I've been three times."

"Go again, it's good for you." I left Aunt Kate about seven in the morning and wandered around the streets. The war had come home to roost.

Part of Stepney Green was destroyed. Single walls stood where houses had once enclosed a family. Beams of wood jutted out at crazy angles.

People were poking about the ruins, pulling out a few precious belongings. Those big black bombers had dropped eggs of death from their bellies. But I didn't have much time to reflect on life and death for a new game was in progress.

The boys of Stepney Green were scrubbing around in the debris near the docktower for pieces of shrapnel. This caught my imagination and immediately I set to it. I found lots of pieces of blue and grey metal and proudly I showed them to another kid. "That bit's no good, it's from an ack-ack gun, but that's all right. That's from a German bomb." I wondered who made the rules but I played the game. I was very pleased with my shrapnel and I rushed home to show my family who were eating and cleaning up and washing and discussing and arguing and I went out again after breakfast, round to Bedmans Road to look for some more. In front of me was a space, where once had been the house of a boy I knew. Not a very close friend, just someone I played with occasionally.

"What happened?" I asked a warden.

"They all got killed."

Funny, I thought, I had seen him only the day before and now he was no more.

When I went home for lunch my father was sitting with his ear against the radio set, twisting the knob around the world until he settled on Germany.

"The Jews of England are either dead or hiding in their holes," a sickening voice snarled over the air.

"That's what you think," my father shouted back.

He still went on about the class war. That the West End hadn't been touched. I asked him why we didn't move there. He dismissed this with "If we had money we'd be all right. Trust the rich."

"It's the same the whole world over, it's the Yids wot get the blame," Uncle Hymie sang. And then, rather incongruously, my father went on about how people always said there was no such thing as a poor Jew, and here in the East End there were over 200,000, all poor and all Jewish. "If only the English people listened to us, had learned from the Yidden, they would have been all right." He went on and on lamenting. But he saw a little ray of hope. After all we have the same enemy, at least Mosley's in prison, so they're waking up at last.

After the terror of that night people started to flock towards the tube. They wanted to get underground. Thousands upon thousands the next evening pushed their way into Liverpool Street Station, demanded to be let down to shelter. At first the authorities wouldn't agree to it and they called out the soldiers to bar the way. I stood there in the thick of the crowd with my mother and father and brothers and sisters thinking that there would be a panic and we would all be crushed to death.

It was the worst experience I had up until then and I wanted to rush out of that crowd, but I was jammed tight. I would have preferred to take my chances in the street with the bombs. Anything was preferable to that crush. I shouted my head off, went limp and was carried along by the surging masses, trying to hold on to my slipping identity. The people would not give up and would not disperse, would not take no for an answer. A great yell went up and the gates were opened and my mother threw her hands together and clutched them towards the sky. "Thank God. He heard me." As if she had a special line through to Him and He had intervened with the government on behalf of the Kops family.

"It's a great victory for the working class," a man said, "One of our big victories."

And though I felt ill and my heart was beating over-fast, all the family were thrilled to know that people had taken over the underground and made the government acquiesce.

So I dashed with the crowd into the underground and saw the solidarity of the surface disappear as an endless stream of people crushed in after us. We were underground people with the smell of disinfectant in our nostrils and blankets under our arms, standing jammed, shoving and pushing each other. No laughter, no humour. What sort of victory had we achieved? Every family for itself now, and my mother tried to encompass all her family with her bulk, a family that had emigrated into the bowels of the earth. Dignity and joy left the world, my world. Shuffling down I felt as if we were fulfiling some awful prophecy. A prophecy that no one had uttered to me. Something that everyone knew but didn't want to talk about.

The soldiers downstairs forced us to get into trains, to go further up the line. Liverpool Street, being the closest, geographically and umbilically, was the most popular. So we were forced to move on and we tried the next station along the Central Line, and then the next and the next.

I heard sirens. And sirens and sirens. Early in the morning, in the afternoon and in the evening. And we went underground to get away from the sirens and the bombs. Yet they followed me and I heard sirens until the world became a siren. One endless cry of torture. It penetrated right into the core of my being, night and day was one long night, one long nightmare, one long siren, one long wail of despair. Some people feel a certain nostalgia for those days, recall a poetic dream about the blitz. They talk about those days as if they were time of a true communal spirit. Not to me. It was the beginning of an era of utter terror, of fear and horror. I stopped being a child and came face to face with the new reality of the world.

I would scoot out of the train ahead of the family and under the legs of people, unravelling the three or four scarves tied around me. And I bagged any space I could along the platform, The family followed, and we pitched our 'tent', then we unravelled and unwound and relaxed. And out came the sandwiches and the forced good humour. Here we were back on the trot — wandering again, involved in a new exodus — the Jews of the East End, who had left their homes, and gone into the exile of the underground. Our spirits would rise for a while, we were alive for another night, we would see another dawn.

Now I see that the miracle of Moses wasn't getting the message from God but in getting all the Jews to go in the same direction, to make them into one big family. For despite the obvious relief and friendliness and the sharing of the sandwiches, families were going in all directions, each trying to feather its own three feet of concrete. And something had been lost without trace. This is what Hitler brought to the world with his commandments. The Jewish people of London with their terrific communal feeling were being torn apart, irrevocably, for all time. But then, so was the whole world.

"This is what they brought to the world," my mother said. And an old man with a sharp beard sitting down next to me, shook his head knowingly. "When they start on the Jews a terrible retribution comes to the world. Look at Haman! Look at Pharaoh!"

But I wasn't only miserable, for seizing advantage of my mother's preoccupations, I managed to get some money out of her. And I got bars and bars of chocolate out of the chocolate machines and weighed myself incessantly. Here was a new life, a whole network, a whole city under the world. We rode up and down the escalators. The children of London were adapting themselves to the times, inventing new games, playing hop-scotch while their mothers shyly suckled young babies on the concrete. And I used to ride backwards and forwards in the trains to see the other stations of underground people.

One night, though, we were very lucky. We were pitched down at Liverpool Street and Phyllis and I (for now Phoebe had decided that her name was old-fashioned) decided to venture as far as Marble Arch. As the train moved out of the Bank Station and entered the tunnel, it stopped and all the lights went out. There was a great thud and we held our ears, When we returned we realised a bomb had fallen down the lift shaft of that station and, apart from those who were killed from blast, there were also those who had been thrown on the line and electrocuted just as our train pulled out.

I was relieved when a few weeks later my mother said she couldn't take it any longer. She decided to leave London with the family. Up until now she was reluctant for my father and Dave couldn't go because of essential war work. Yes, even my father, almost as blind as a bat, was of some use. And he was glad. Jack was in the army, so it was just the girls, me and my Mother who were leaving.

"Yes, I'll get Rose from Denham, and we'll go up North," she said.

I slept more peacefully on the stone that night.

Two days later we left London.

* * *

Blood is Thicker Than Water

The Kops family entered Leeds and we found a flat in a street of prostitutes. Nice girls who always smiled at me. I became a lather boy in a barber shop in Chapeltown Road. One night I heard my mother say, "He's the one to take me out of the slums. You'll see. He's the one to buy me the house."

Her faith in me made me angry. I felt more and more caught in a trap.

Every morning I had to be dragged out of bed.

"Don't you see. How can I get you out of the slums if I'm a lousy barber. I don't want to be a bloody barber."

The sirens that night saved me. This time it was the most beautiful sound in the world. No work tomorrow I thought. We sheltered beneath the synagogue, my mother repeating every few minutes. "What am I doing in Leeds if there's an air raid? This is no good to me at all."

I agreed with her. "They say there are terrible raids on Hull and now the Germans are going to concentrate on the North of England."

Well, they did drop a few bombs on Leeds. This was enough for me to work on so I built them up into an Armageddon.

I told her that someone said they heard the Germans were going to concentrate on Leeds.

"Why should I get bombed in Leeds when I can get bombed in London?" She couldn't bear to be parted from the rest of the family any longer. That was obvious. Just before Christmas she decided we were going back.

"Bombs or no bombs, we're going back to London."

So I said goodbye to the upside down faces and the barber. God bless him, I don't think. Goodbye to the birds of Briggate with their homely come-hither look, and to the delicatessen shops of Chapeltown Road.

We were returning to the thick of it, to the blitz of London and I was convinced that we would all be killed. Anyway, I thought, that would solve my problems.

So ended the Yorkshire episode of half the Kops family, for blood is thicker than water, and in my mother's words, "What's the good of a family if it's separated?"

There was little welcome when we got back. Everybody was white in the face and silent.

Except my Dad. "So what did you come home for?" he said. "We're being bombed to smithereens." Then he chastised me for giving up a good job.

London was completely transformed. There were great gaps of jagged space where houses once stood. And we returned to Stepney Green for a while. Now I was no longer worried about my future but more about day-to-day survival. No longer did I collect shrapnel but leapt for shelter as soon as the sirens went. A taste of salt came to my mouth and fear made my eyes twitch. All feeling of community had completely faded. We were all withdrawn into ourselves. Little furtive groups of families groping between shelter and home. There was still a superficial sort of friendliness on the surface, but the roots had been cut. The Jewish community, the family, the spirit, had died. And it was never reborn, not exactly the way it was. An essential ingredient was lost for ever. The inner sense of belonging, together.

"It's all gone. All gone, Everything we ever had is finished. What's happened to us? Oh, by my mother in the grave, what is going to become of us?" That was the way my mother cried. And I no longer tried to overtake people in the streets. On the contrary I stood nervously at junctions wondering, "If I go down that way, I might get killed by a bomb. On the other hand, if I walk along Stepney Green, on the other side of the road, I might get hit by a bit of shrapnel. Which way do I go?" Every step was a decision and every decision may have been the wrong one.

My sister Essie lived in Gold Street, just along Stepney Green, and the night after our return we sheltered in her Anderson in the garden. It was terrible in there. I shivered one moment and sweltered the next. Later that night we had enough so we went indoors. This time there was no comic relief from my uncles, just a night of sheer terror. The wail and the howl and the scream and the crash. The body of the world was being cremated, pounded, crushed and scattered in space. I looked out at the sky from an empty bedroom. A firework display of death-planes were caught in the fingers of searchlights that poked the sky. In the other room my sisters cried and my mother was shaking her white face at the looking glass, "Why? Why? What have we done?" I put my hand against one of the walls. It was almost red hot. I rushed outside and found the house immediately next door burning down. And the whole street alight. All around was flame and we just couldn't do a thing but stand and watch the street burn down. But my sister's house wasn't touched. It stood alone in a blackened blazing wilderness that yesterday was called Gold Street.

Fortunately all the people of the street were down the underground. The night was hell, where we rushed around each other, hands over ears, clenching eyes, asking, imploring each other, "How long will it last?" "Are we going to die?" "Tell me it's gonna be all right." The night-bombers hurried away when the first strands of dawn appeared.

What struck me in the morning was the complete absence of people. I managed to find a Yiddisher bakery open nearby and bought some hot *platzels* and took them home.

We never got caught by the sirens again, at least not in the evening. We moved away forever from Stepney Green and we never returned.

We moved to Bethnal Green where we spent our hours of day, and in the late afternoon we would make for the underground, with our bundles of blankets. For every day we had to claim our few feet of concrete. The constant worry was whether we would find a space for that night. We lived only for four o'clock when they let us down, when we would hurtle into the underworld, into the trains of the Central Line. Often we would find each station already full up. People ahead of us, who were all fixed up, looked so smug as we panicked around for a vacant slab of stone. You couldn't blame them. We were the same anyway, once we got settled under the burning streets of London. Each night we lived under a different district: Marble Arch, Holborn, Oxford Circus, St Paul's. We never bothered to venture away from the Central Line even though I believe the Northern Line was deeper.

Our one night at St Paul's was terribly memorable. Smoke poured down and a boy dared me to go upstairs with him. I was dead scared but felt compelled to do so. At the top of the escalator the warden warned us not to venture out but we slipped past for a few moments and I stood in the entrance for no more than a few seconds. The whole of the City of London was alight. We rushed down again. I didn't tell my mother what I had seen, and I lay down in silence and didn't sleep the whole night long.

But sometimes we couldn't make the underground for the air-raids started in the morning and went on all day.

We now lived in my sister's house in Brick Lane which had a surface brick shelter at the back of the yard.

When we couldn't get underground a feeling of dread overcame me, for apart from everything else my mother was cracking up. One day in particular I slipped out of the shelter during a quiet patch to get a bit of food. When I returned the bombers were overhead again. My brother-in-law Mick was an air-raid warden and he was standing there among a crowd of people from my sister's buildings. Shells were bursting in the sky.

"What are you doing?" Mick demanded. "Get into the shelter. You'll all be killed."

'We prefer to take our chances outside with the bombs," an old man said. "We can't stand Mrs Kops and her daughter having hysterics inside." I could hear my mother and sister screaming their heads off. Mick went into the shelter, shouting at them.

60

They stopped, but oh I remember my mother's look of terror as she cuddled my sister. That night! I and my brother were larking about in a passage of the building, when we were thrown off our feet by a rushing wind. I never heard a sound but my ears went funny, yet apparently the crash was heard for miles around.

A landmine had dropped on Columbia Market shelter two hundred yards away. It fell straight through the lift shaft and exploded down there. I saw a policeman come out weeping and carrying a dead child. It was the first time I had seen anybody dead.

"Cry," my mother said, "It will make you feel better." But I couldn't. Blood was thicker than water all right and all the blood within me was crying out. For opposite, the houses were no more and people I knew were no more.

The King of England came the following morning, drawn and grey he walked slowly over the wreckage. No one cheered because they didn't feel like cheering. But when Churchill came a few hours later, with a cigar sticking out of his fat pink face, a few people did cheer and even I felt like cheering. But I didn't. Despite Noel Coward's song, 'Every Blitz your resistance stubborning!' My mother's strength was failing fast and she just couldn't take much more and we finally persuaded her to leave London again.

You won't keep me away!" she kept on saying, even at the station. Again and again she implored me to go away with her. I told her I couldn't.

I wanted to be on my own, away from the East End. I wanted to think things out for myself. I had to go in another direction, away from the family. I had managed to get a job in one of the big hotels in the West End, as an apprentice cook.

I was going to have my tall white hat after all. The other attractive thing about working in a hotel was that the West End didn't seem to be getting bashed so badly. As we stood waiting for the train to leave I told her about my new job, thought she'd be delighted. My father was.

"You don't need to work!" My mother implored me until the last moment. The train drew out and we hardly waved. Blood was thicker than water, for despite being fifteen and cynical, I cried.

Off they went in the direction of Ipswich and I wandered through the East End alone, getting rid of my father at Aldgate East.

"Take care of yourself, boy!"

"Yes Dad." That's all you needed to say. "Yes Dad. No Dad." I felt somehow close to him as I walked away, very close and very guilty. We shook hands. It was an act of strangers.

I walked to Stepney Green and climbed the seven flights of the Buildings and stood on the landing, outside the deserted house. I looked over the East End, the deserted quiet streets. All the children were evacuated. The railings of the park had been torn out to be made into shells and guns and bombs. The world as I knew it had passed away. It had died. Gone mad and died. Mr Lindsberg's sweet shop was no longer there. Esther the sweet woman was no longer there, Gold Street where my sister had lived had gone up in smoke. Redmans Road and Stepney Green had become a wasteland of rubble and mounds of earth, of broken springs and furniture and broken homes. Faces I once knew came flooding back to my swimming eyes. Faces of people now dead.

I could hear the tap dripping into the sink of the scullery of my deserted house, so I rushed down the stairs and ran towards the main road, towards the West End, towards my new life and my tall white hat.

But I stopped on the way and stood on the bombed site of the family I knew who had been wiped out a year before. The fireplace still stood like a tombstone surrounded by the cemetery of Stepney.

Weeds grew where children once played. Nature returns so soon to reclaim the earth abused by people. But blood is thicker than water. I was alive and wanted to live, so I shrugged and walked away.

———————————

My Giddy Aunts

I always knew when Passover was imminent because of the gathering of aunts. We would play hide-and-seek around the furniture and they would all be huddled around a table, excitable, exchanging addresses. My mother called them the *'schnorroring* letters.' Out they would go to obscure Jewish societies telling them of our plight in Stepney Green, the possibility of a *Pesach* without food.

All my aunts talked all of the time, if not to each other, to themselves.

"I've got a good address for you."

"These people last year sent me a lovely bottle of wine."

"If you're lucky they'll send you a jar of rollmops."

"I even got a stuffed monkey."

My mouth was already watering. Visions of the cupboard at last having some tins of salmon and condensed milk. It was the only time of the year you could rely on going to bed with a full stomach.

"Don't forget to go to the Dutch Consul. Didn't he give you two pounds last year? Oh yes, and Mrs Gershon at the Beaumont Square Girls' Club, for some bread, meat and coal tickets."

My mother was an old hand at this. Next week I would be queueing up with her outside Great Garden Street Synagogue. That mile-long queue wouldn't daunt us, because at the end of it was Shangri-la — a box of Bonn's *matzos*.

Thus they conspired to make ends meet for the special occasion. You could rest assured that soon the different charities would be putting parcels in the post: eggs, sugar, wine, *matzo*-meal, sweets, biscuits.

The business done, the aunts would start whispering among themselves, mouthing words across the table, my mother pointing to my sister, and all the aunts nodding. "Really, she started? When did she come on?"

It was all double-Dutch to me. This was the tribal time, the time I loved. In those days families extended for ever and ever. Everything that happened to everyone seemed significant.

First published in the *Jewish Chronicle* magazine (1987)

"Did you hear what happened to Morry? He got hit over the head with a truncheon outside Simpson's."

"The bastard, guess what he did? He took her into the stock room and took liberties."

Gasps of horror, heads shaking in disbelief. Families meant hundreds of people, all close, all involved. If it was claustrophobic you thrived on it. This seemed the only true sustenance; you were closer to joy and sorrow. Cousins were everywhere. One died, Jack, of Bright's Disease. When they carried his small coffin out and down from the Buildings, I remember looking up and there were faces staring from every window. Their crying sounded like singing.

The letters written, the parcels arriving, my mother got a Wickham's Clothing Cheque; it was the only time of the year we would know new clothes and, more often than not, my new suit would be pawned as soon as Passover was over. My mother lived more than a hand-to-mouth existence. It was a hand-to-head existence. "How am I going to manage?" she cried.

Passover arrived. It was the peak of our year. It smelled differently from all other times. The almonds and cinnamon being mixed in the kitchen, and my mother making the food of the gods, *gremsels*. And as fast as she fried them, you pinched them from the plate. "They're driving me mad, I don't know what I'm doing." And my father in a reverie, bringing to life some atavistic Dutch Jewish custom, sprinkling brown sugar on *matzo*, pouring tea on top and devouring it in mouthfuls and then the *matzo brei* — egg and *matzos* mashed together and fried.

We weren't religious, we didn't have a *seder*, but we had chicken soup and *kneidlech* with stuffed neck of chicken. When you're so poor, getting enough to eat sometimes becomes your religion. We almost had no time for anything else. But this was a feast and every face was happy.

How clean I was! My knees were scrubbed, my hair was smarted down, and I rushed down into the playground, all seven flights, three steps at a time. I had a bag of cracker-nuts in my pocket, and I was all set for one of the great adventures of life.

In that playground were all the kids who lived in the Buildings, my friends and enemies, my cousins, sisters and brothers, and all of us looked beautiful. We laughed and pointed, not believing the vision of each other. I built a castle with my

64

cracker-nuts. "Who wants a castle? Knock down my castle." I soon became a capitalist, for every castle of four nuts knocked down I seemed to have acquired at least thirty. Soon my pockets were bulging.

The whole day was spent at this ritual, and flirting. The girls were so beautiful, and I saw them in a new light, with their long hair gleaming, and their long dresses billowing out as they twirled and danced. Later we went from aunt to aunt, to each house to get a silver sixpence. I looked forward to the sixpence, but not to the aunt. It was like running the gauntlet. Each aunt would twist the flesh of your cheek and smother you with wet kisses. "Isn't he beautiful, I could eat him."

That year I must have collected more than three shillings. It was a fortune, I would be a millionaire for the rest of the year. I would be able to go to the pictures, to the Rivoli, next week, the week after. I would be able to buy a top and maybe get a sixpenny all-day ticket for a tram-ride beyond my world.

I still remember those cracker-nuts. I would take them to bed with me, find secret places to hide them. But some would end up in the pawn shop, hidden in the lining of my new suit; now lost forever. The memory of Passover lasted for the rest of the year and then in January it would soon be the gathering of the aunts again, exchanging addresses for the Passover to come. We belonged, and sure we were desperately poor, but somehow the real poverty came later when most of us did well and moved away.

Hackney! Sunday! Rain!

Hackney! Sunday! Rain! You know the sort of day.

Black empty trees against a desolate sky.
Expressionless people buying sad daffodils outside the hospital,
people unaccustomed to flowers except for births marriages
    and death.

So many people come into this place
and so many go out, you know how,
and have their first contact with the earth
in God knows how long.

And here my father is going to die.
I walk to his bed where he smiles at me
although he is already dead,
his milk-white eyes taking,
taking their last look at the world.
He moans, over and over again.
Why? Why am I here? I have no pain.

He has nothing now to tell us, we his gathered children.
A nondescript life sliding into oblivion,
a nobody going nowhere, becoming no-one,
like everyone.
Yet death brings his face distinction,
breeding tells and his skull showing through
is as good as anyone's.

Cancer! Whisper it! Do not let him hear.
Have you seen the doctor? Is there any hope?
What did the sister say? Someone said someone worse than him
lived for another year.
How long? How long? How long do you think it will take?

I look out of the window.
Who knows, perhaps he can outlast the world.

From *Erica, I Want to Read You Something* (1967)

66

Haven't you noticed a sudden deterioration
in almost everything?

The body of the world seems to be wasting away,
the face and the heart and the brain seem to decay.
Yet we pray and hope or try to hope and pray,
try to remove the growth to live for another day.

Guilty, that I am not; grieving, because I cannot,
I run out into the world,
try to whistle, try not to weep.

And quickly get the tube away....

from **By the Waters of Whitechapel**

Whitechapel appeared more squashed than usual. The poky side-streets all seemed pinched together. Nevertheless Aubrey was pleased to be home.

Bournemouth out of season had been as much as he could bear. Even the deserted Commercial Road seemed quite jolly in comparison to that graveyard. They walked at a funereal pace through the smoggy morning, Leah stopping every few yards or so to blow out, breathe in, and to clutch at her heart.

Some mothers had the decency to die between sixty-five and seventy. But then, she was not just anyone. She was Leah the Feld.

Aubrey knew why she liked to walk the mile to Hessel Street. It would put her into her mood of happy discontent for the rest of the day. She loved to mourn her shrinking silhouette in shop windows. Her face was either tilted up towards her invisible god, or it was nodding down at the pavements where her ghosts seemed to cram each inch of space just beneath her own minute height. Only the dead seemed to appreciate what Leah had to put up with.

She started muttering to herself again, so he smiled and gazed beyond her, his vision towering above the mongol houses that squatted in rows along the decaying streets.

"If only you did not depend upon me, Mother." This time he spoke directly at her. The days when he feared this woman were as dead as the East End of London. But all she did was to continue her inaudible dialogue with her own dead.

They were nearly home now and when they reached Christian Street he took her wrist. It was no thicker than the neck of a chicken waiting for the plucker.

"Aubrey! You're stopping my circulation."

He released her and the usual sickening depression descended upon the world, covering his whole doomed domain. Three skinny neurotic pigeons pecked at the cold concrete. "Look at those *nebbich* pigeons," he said. Then he forgot all about them. "Mother —" he would allow himself the luxury of just one moan

From *By the Waters of Whitechapel*, a novel (1969)

"Mother, what is the meaning of me? What is my *raison d'être*?"

She looked concerned, "Don't worry, dolly — soon be home."

They turned the corner into Hessel Street. Aubrey could see their pathetic little sweetshop at the other end.

"Why do you make me work for you? Have I been such a bad son?"

"Do you want my honest opinion, or the truth?" Leah laughed.

He pretended that she had not spoken. "I want my life to bear fruit," he answered, opening his hands in the manner of his ancestors.

"At thirty-nine you should be driving a wife mad and not your mother. At thirty-nine."

"Thirty-five!" he hissed back. "If you don't mind."

Then he decided to be compassionate. How could anyone expect a silly old woman to understand the blazing dreams of youth? "I do love you, Mother, but your life is nearly over."

"That's what you think," Leah replied with satisfaction.

"I must start thinking about my future," he said.

"Shut up," she snapped.

So he did; and it was a pleasure.

By now they stood outside the sweetshop, which should have been shuttered. Aubrey could understand his mother's sudden concern. After all it was not only a question of the stock within, not just jars and jars of sweets on the shelves and the stacks of cigarettes. Beyond the shop and above it was their home. Everything they possessed in this life existed behind these walls.

"Someone's inside! Someone's inside! Get the police." Leah's frightened voice cut through his meanderings and through the noise of the Pakistani opera seeping from the house next door, as it had done, without a break, since the autumn of 1960.

She pushed against the door. "Should be locked. Shout for the police," she screamed as the door opened and the doorbell pinged.

Deep in the gloom of the interior he could see Auntie Beattie; economising with the electricity as usual.

"Who's there? Who's there?" Leah took up a full jar of sherbet lemons and held it high above her head, with shaking claws.

"Hello, Auntie Beattie," Aubrey said, switching on the light.

"Leah — why you back so soon? Thought you were staying a week." Auntie Beattie's melancholy voice was enough to

69

reassure Leah. She replaced the jar of sweets and seemed glad that her sister had not seen. This was hardly surprising since Auntie Beattie could barely see her own five fingers if she held them up close against her own nose. Still, despite acute myopia, she handled the till all right. As she always said: "Money's like neon. It lights up."

"Didn't you like Bournemouth? I told you not to worry about the shop."

"I'm so glad to see you here, Beattie." Leah went behind the counter and the sisters kissed, each leaving a scarlet cupid bow on the other's cheek.

"Course I'm here. Where else should I be?"

Leah sighed and nodded and sighed and so did Beattie; sighing was the Esperanto of the Jewish race. In the hierarchy of primitive Yiddish sounds, the sigh reigned supreme.

Leah sat down behind the counter and took a mug of tea from her sister's flask. "So how's business? Taken anything? Ain't it lovely to be home, Aubrey?"

She was always like that, never waiting for a reply. Auntie Beattie was pouring out a cup of tea for him.

"No thank you, Auntie. No thank you."

But she still pushed the drink towards him. He didn't want to hurt her feelings so he started sipping it.

"So I did right, eh? Opening up? You're surprised. Admit. How could I rest if my one and only sister was losing all her customers? So I did right?"

"You did what I expected you to do. But why no customers?"

"What's a sister for if she can't look after a sweetshop? Specially when you had to go away to the coast to stop your highly-strung son having a nervous breakdown."

"How dare you imply such a thing?" Aubrey stomped out of the shop and into the even gloomier living room beyond.

"Hope you soon feel better, Aub," Auntie Beattie shouted after him and then her pink clean face came round the door, her mouth was opened wide and she laughed and laughed.

"Shut up. Just shut up." He shot away from the blob of flabby flesh and closed his eyes.

"I'm so pleased you're better. So delighted you're behaving civil at last. You don't seem the same boy. Keep it up, please God."

He looked round and hissed.

But she was waving. "Toodleloo. Have a rest." Then Beattie returned to Leah and they continued the autopsy on the dead morning.

He watched them for a while through the open door. People said there was a great family likeness; certainly there was not much to choose between either of them. They were both bloody ugly. But then, it was his own flesh and blood so he was naturally biased.

"It's good to be home, but I'll die without tea. Can't understand. No customers? Not a single customer?"

"I put nothing in the till, believe me. And I put nothing nowhere else."

"Beattie! Please! How could you say such a thing? Would I think such things about you?"

"Na! Only joking. So what happened? Why did you come home?"

"Must make more tea." She was about to hurry through into the kitchen but she turned to her smiling younger sister. "You're a good girl, Beattie. A girl in a million. I hope you don't leave me for the rest of the day. I couldn't manage otherwise."

Leah scooted through the living room. "Tea with lemon, Aubrey. You'll feel better."

There was a sudden calm, and he opened his eyes, feeling totally unafraid of this room where he had been born. Yes, he, Aubrey Field, had actually fallen out of the universe into this ridiculous little existence via Leah Feld. He had grown up here behind these walls and played dark and light games and grown out of shoes in this very living room.

He had not been born upstairs in bed like other people, up above the cracked stained ceiling where the flies were making love. Leah did not have time to get to the bedroom. "For once in your life, Aubrey, you were in a hurry. You couldn't wait." She said this over and over again, "You just couldn't wait."

"Wonder why?"

He did not wipe away the tears that assembled in each eye. It was probably onions anyway, if either his mother or aunt were peeling some, which was not unlikely.

He looked beyond Leah in the kitchen. No, he had never been convinced that he knew the entire story concerning his origins.

He looked beyond the house, beyond the street outside the window, beyond the world where a boat was wailing somewhere along the pea-soup river.

Beyond-beyond. To places without names and ideas without words.

Then he remembered that his toenails needed cutting. So he cut them.

Completing this satisfying task, Aubrey was disappointed. He loved the sound of nail flying in all directions and he wondered if just one piece had managed to reach as far as the kitchen and hit her just enough to remind her that he could wait not a minute longer for tea. Then he closed his eyes and decided to let everything flow over him. But when he opened them again, Leah had deserted the asthmatic kettle for the shop.

Leah stopped counting the stock and looked out at the lonely street.

"No one's about," Beattie said, leaning over her sister's shoulder, pushing her pebbled glasses right up against the window glass.

"No one? You should live so long," Leah ridiculed. "It's thick out there, with ghosts, memories!"

Beattie went back to the security behind the counter, but Leah continued talking. "They never leave you alone. Ghost dustmen; ghost coalmen; ghost *beigel* women; ghost *schnorrers*; ghost *bubas*. Then suddenly you realise you're all alone; everyone you knew or didn't want to know has been *shlepped* right out of the street and taken for a ride to Marlowe Road Burial Ground, East Ham, London E17."

"Mother, don't be morbid. Be miserable if you like —"

But Leah hadn't heard him.

"Funny! As you walk along you see all the faces from the past. People you never lowered yourself to talk to, you now accept. You even cuddle them. You're glad and grateful they don't look right through you. You invite them inside for a little bit of homemade cheesecake. But of course — they can't come."

"Good job too; price of cheesecake." Beattie was used to Leah's sudden journeys into the unseen world of yesterday.

Leah came back down to earth; which was almost a fact, considering how thin and rotten the floorboards were. "No one about? Good job you can't see proper, Beattie. It's thicker than a flypaper out there. You can cut through with a breadknife." She laughed and then laughed at herself laughing and returned to the hub of her universe.

In the kitchen she made tea. "Think we'll have a nice drop of *lokshen* soup, later," she called to her sister.

"Just as well I bought a boiler, eh? It's in the fridge." Beattie lit up for having done the right thing. Leah gave Aubrey his glass of lemon tea and then opened the fridge. "Lovely bird; it'll make a lovely drop of soup."

"Your soup never varies, Leah. You make the best chicken soup in London."

"For once I must agree with you, Beattie. I admit I'm good at many things, but nothing can touch my boiled fowl. I'll put it on soon." Leah smiled back. Aubrey couldn't stand the conversation a moment longer so he went into the sweetshop and opened a lucky bag.

It contained three minute cubes of dolly mixture, which he swallowed without chewing. He found a little plastic plane in the bag so he hurled it into the dirty sky above Hessel Street, forgetting to open the window. It nose-dived and lay crushed under Auntie Beattie's rather eccentric-looking plimsolls.

Aubrey opened the window to enjoy the final item the lucky bag contained: a party hat in pink and pale blue. It fitted his generous head so he kept it on and looked down Hessel Street, eyeing either end in turn, like a Wimbledon spectator.

"Aubrey!" she screamed. "Your tea is waiting to warm you up." But when she saw the party hat she shook her head. "Why does an Aubrey happen to a good woman like me?"

Auntie Beattie watched the two of them as she popped one lemon sherbet after another into her mouth.

"Stop eating the stock, Beattie. Eating the profits is no good for teeth. Even false." Then she turned to her son, despatching a sorrowful little wave. "Haven't I done enough? Haven't I slaved enough for you? Can you complain? Haven't I given you everything you needed?"

He nodded his loving agreement but continued thinking. Life was very tenuous. Your skeleton followed you everywhere; like an understudy, waiting for you to break your neck so that it could take over.

Leah stood at the sink watching for a saucepan to boil, and like most other mortals she didn't realise how close she was to death. She could slip and her whole head could go right into that large saucepan of bubbling water and her hard-boiled eyeballs would turn white and her tongue would peel. Or she could just as easily faint over the washing and her head go down beneath the foam. Someone so easily, so gently, could give her a little push forward and hold her head under foaming detergent.

"Why are you laughing?" Leah said. "What you got to laugh about?"

Aubrey dismissed his frivolous thoughts. Who in his right mind would want to drown his own dear mother in a sink of suds?

Yet he felt a certain compassion for people who needed to do such horrid deeds. For sometimes the world misconstrued the real motive. People would be quick to condemn him for releasing her from this tormented world. Who would try and understand that he was merely thinking of her? For was there really any point in her continuing to live in this cruel world of indifference, plague, and drunken driving? Did society care a damn for the aged? To what did Leah have to look forward? Senility? Kosher meals on wheels?

"So go to the table; or do I take the table to you? Let's all have a snack," she said, carrying packets, containers, utensils and plates to the living room.

"You have. I'm not hungry," he replied, squeezing a blackhead that wasn't there the day before.

"Beattie? If you're not busy serving you may as well eat," she called. "Just a snack."

Beattie trotted out of the empty shop. "I'm already sitting down," she said, sitting down, closely observing all the usual delicacies as Leah laid them on the table.

"Don't worry, Mother." Aubrey continued gazing out of the window at absolutely nothing.

"Worried? Who's worried? What you staring at out there? Day after day."

Beattie shushed her sister rather noisily. "So he's a bit *meshugger*. So we have to humour him and make the most of a bad job." She would have called her remark a whisper.

"Wish I was in my grave. Matter of fact I wish I was dead," Leah replied, slurping spoonfuls of cold borsht down her own thankful throat.

Aubrey turned to his mother and smiled like a photo. "You know I'll always take care of you," he cooed from far away.

But Leah wasn't listening to him. "Eat then, Beattie. Don't you like it?" There was more threat than concern in her voice.

"Yes, yes. Of course," Beattie replied hurriedly.

"Eat then. Anyone would think I never give you no food."

"It's very nice of you," Aubrey heard his auntie reply.

"Yes, it is. But after all you are my sister. Why should I leave you out? You ain't committed a murder or something like that. Beautiful chopped herring."

Then Aubrey noticed something for the very first time. His mother's jugular vein stood out prominently. It was like an undulating river. Or a serpent. He could not take his fascinated eyes from the fearful little snake. One little snip, with nail scissors, and all her blood would gush out from her interior. And she would be dead. But not unkosher.

"Perish the thought." He shuddered.

"Perish all thought. You thought too much. Eat better." She looked down in adoration at the tribal table. "Thinking will be your downfall," she added during a voluble mouthful. "This new green cucumber is the best I ever tasted, even if I do say so myself. After all, I made it."

Leah finished eating before her sister had started and she stretched her skeleton and yawned contentedly to confirm the well-being she was suddenly experiencing. But then she clutched her head and heart and grimaced as if she were exaggerating a smile. "Oh, I got pain everywhere."

He watched her without emotion. One had to stand back sometimes from those one loved. Perhaps she would really die during this spasm; perhaps she would fall down on the floor, go dark blue in the face and explode.

Aubrey did not feel ashamed of his thoughts. He knew that he personally would not harm a single strand of hair upon his mother's head. Of course he did not hate her, although she sometimes got on his nerves. As a matter of fact he was quite grateful to her. After all, she had done her best for him, and once she even paid for tennis and driving lessons. He never really wanted her to die either by natural causes or strangulation. He had never done a single thing to be ashamed of as far as his sweet mother was concerned. Nobody could point the finger and say that he did not rank amongst the most devoted sons in the whole dark world.

Thoughts about her possible and imminent death merely arose out of his philosophical conviction that people should not be allowed to live beyond sixty-five. He personally welcomed the idea of being despatched by a helping hand before he approached the seventies. Anyone, but anyone, would be doing him a service if they pushed him in front of a train on the Central Line or sprinkled strychnine on his instant porridge.

But he was no dogmatic bigot. Other people probably had other ideas and they were perfectly entitled to them. There was no doubt that some people actually enjoyed living beyond sixty, and he was the first person to accede to their legitimate if ridiculous desire. It took all sorts —.

"Aubrey! Stop staring at nothing," Leah croaked, sucking up very slowly her own glass of lemon tea.

"Yes, Aubrey. You look pale. You've got a pallor. If you must stare at something at least stare at the steam of the tea." Auntie Beattie winked intimately at her sister and nudged her. "And in an hour *lokshen* soup. One sniff of your mum's cooking and you'll surrender." She spread chopped liver over a slice of rye bread.

"My part. I should care. Forget him, Beattie. His own tea's stone cold and all the goodness is gone. But who cares? His funeral."

He decided to join them, so he walked over slowly and sat down whilst his eyes gazed up at the ceiling. It wasn't good to let your mother know just how practical and down-to-earth you really were. It was always imperative to hold the real you in secrecy and reserve. "So where's my smoked salmon?"

She laughed and twisted the flesh of his cheek. "I love your *chutzpah*. I've got some special for you." She trotted to the gas stove to make him more tea and she hummed a tune that had headed the charts twelve weeks before. It was eminently forgettable but he remembered it because he remembered all things.

"Oh Mother," Aubrey spoke to air through the vacant smiling head of Auntie Beattie, "what is the meaning of me? What is my *raison d'être?'*

"Shan't be a tick," she called from the kitchen. "Don't get impatient."

"Impatient!" His lush resonant reply echoed through the entire house and was followed by a sardonic and iconoclastic laugh. "I want to escape. If only you would let me go. Mother, Mother."

"He's very clever. I always said so," Auntie Beattie said.

"Oh God, what would happen to you if I went? If only you would release me, Mother."

Leah hurried back and placed the plate of pink gold before him. "Thirty-five shillings a pound," she said, standing back to admire the best Scotch smoked salmon, and her son, who cost her even more.

"Please. Please let me go." His voice was full of compassion.

"He's so overstrung though." Beattie shook her smiling head and went back into the shop.

"Eat up," Leah said, feeling his forehead, "and later you can have a little doze. You need your rest."

Automatically he started to eat the delicious fishy flesh. His hand and mouth were programmed for delicatessen. His mind was free but his body belonged to his ancestors; he was addicted to the necessities that sustained them. It was useless, he was trapped. She would never let him go.

"I've been thinking. We must discuss your future. One day perhaps you'll leave home. One day, *aluvi*, you'll fend for yourself. You'll go and stop driving me mad."

He refused to listen anymore. She always spoke more or less like this.

He uttered his loud and long sardonic laugh, the laugh of a man sentenced to life imprisonment. If only she really meant it.

Aubrey continued knocking back the not unpleasurable delicacy, moaning quietly between each devoured mouthful, "If only you would let me. If only you would let me go."

* * *

The day was not entirely a financial disaster. Auntie Beattie and Leah were soon busy dispensing packets of doomtubes to those who actually didn't mind paying for the pleasure of a painful death.

And quite apart from cigarettes, there were also the countless bottles of Tizer, bags of crisps, icelollies, jars and jars of sweets and dollops of petrified plastic called ice-cream.

Aubrey watched the customers from a corner, and he laughed. You had your choice. You departed from the salubrious Borough of Tower Hamlets from fatty heart, rotting mouth, or cancer of the lungs. Or, if you were strong enough, like Aubrey Field, you could choose your own method of suicide; or even die of old age, if you had that much patience.

A sense of calm descended over the shop as the money poured in.

The procession of kids edged slowly forward to the counter, but its length did not diminish. And when the children were actually close to being served, they thrust their arms ahead, as if reaching for Mecca. They all looked so scrubbed clean and their clothes were so spotless. A picture of bygone Hessel Street kids flashed to his mind. "Where are the snotty noses of yesteryear?" Aubrey intoned.

Beattie and Leah were taking money hand over fist, but their faces seemed more appropriate for the end of the world. "Every day's the same. No-one. Then suddenly — everyone! All wanting to be served first."

But the sweating elderly sisters were equal to their task and coping admirably with the sudden rush of customers and heartburn.

In the gloom Aubrey boomed dramatically, "Never send to know for whom the till tolls, it tolls for thee."

"Poetry suddenly! It's foggy outside and he spouts," Auntie Beattie said, as she smiled across to her nephew to show she really didn't mind his special form of madness.

"Shut up, Beattie. And serve." Leah chided her sister and then bullied the sea of frail sepia faces beneath her: "I've only got one pair of hands! What do you want of my life? I'll stop serving altogether."

He wondered why she needed to complain. No one questioned her dynasty, nor her ruling rod of iron over her kingdom. She loved her position in the area, and she was as accepted and secure as Tower Bridge.

His mother had lived by sweets and she would die by sweets. Perhaps one day she might even have the good manners to choke on a bull's eye. God forbid. But if she did, he had nothing to be ashamed of. He would throw a party for all the kids of the neighbourhood. It would probably even be reported on the front page of the *East London Advertiser*. With pictures.

He could just see her lying on a bed of coconut-ice, almost entirely covered with Smarties. She would love that.

And he would stuff a sherbet fountain into her mouth and stick two shiny black Pontefract cakes over her eyes. And he would use two splendid liquorice whirls for a moustache, and stick one red lollipop into each of her ears to give colour to her serene complexion.

And he would bury her like that, taking all the children to the cemetery, where they'd all play Postman's Knock, Kiss-chase, and Blind Man's Buff.

On the way to the burial and on the way back he would provide unlimited fizzy lemonade and crisps. And the children would sing merrily and wave at everyone.

He came back down to shop, where the queue had come to an end.

She had never escaped from E1 and neither would he escape, and Hessel Street would still be standing long after all his mother's and his flesh had been picked clean by the better-class Jewish worms who had exclusive subcontracting rights with the Marlowe Road Burial Ground.

A doe-eyed Pakistani doll floated into the shop followed by an avalanche of brothers and sisters. He knew the children well. They were all hooked on jelly babies.

What would become of these children? Would they escape from these streets where not a solitary tree had the *chutzpah* to grow? Would they ever discover that the sky was larger than a matchbox?

Probably! They'd make it somehow to Slough, Carshalton, or even Guildford. Everyone would escape this noose of streets, except Leah, Auntie Beattie and himself. Only the three of them and the lucky bags would remain.

"Come away from the open door, darling. You'll die. The wind comes straight up the river and turns left at Cable Street."

He stayed looking at the congealing sky, stroking his chin. "I think I'll grow a beard."

"When I'm dead, then you can grow a beard." She laughed and walked towards him, nodding.

Leah's face came right up close, like a zoom lens on television. She reminded him of a camel he once saw at the Bristol Zoo. She was a very nice beast and who could deny that he loved her dearly? She was his mother and deserved only the very best gratitude for all she had sacrificed from the day he had been banished from that horrible cosy dark womb into these dingy commercial outer-outer suburbs of Paradise.

"Without you I'd be free of you. After all, I do have my own life to live." There! He was at it again.

"So live it. There's the door. Outside is the street. One street leads to another. Before you know where you are you'll be miles away." She smacked him gently on the cheek several times, smiled and forwarded a pouted kiss.

"Oh Mother, how subtly you weave your spell." There was simply no point in trying to escape on such a cold day, anyway.

Leah went back to her counter, where her hands started moving back and forth, doling out packets and bags of pleasant poison. Aubrey followed her behind the counter, and stood with one hand clutching the richer sections of his hair.

Baldness would become him, would emphasise his uniquely high forehead. Anyway he would never be entirely bald. The grave, fortunately, would intervene long before anyone would guess that he was indeed much nearer to Yul Brynner than Samson.

"Anyway, if I'm so useless, why do you put up with me?" He hoped she wouldn't see his fingers crawling spiderlike, up one glass sweet jar in order to extract a really delicious-looking piece of pink and white coconut-ice.

"So, Beattie, as I was saying about Bournemouth, the food was out of this world, but the waiters were from another world." When there were customers in the shop Leah just continued talking to her sister about life, death and rheumatism. She served them but ignored them. It was as if they were invisible until the time came for them to pay.

"I put up with you because I'm your mother. Who else would stand for you?" By this time he had almost forgotten his question. "Who'll look after you when I'm gone? Mind you, I'll probably live longer than you," she continued, "Specially if you keep eating coconut-ice."

It slackened off later and Aubrey returned to his one and only hobby, watching the street. A smell of joss sticks hovered on the smoggy air, and this, blended with curry, made him want to hold his nose. Instead he pressed it flat against his face with the palm of his hand. Three black men passed. They were laughing at some private joke, their bodies bending almost to the pavement, which normally does not hear human laughter so close.

"Why shouldn't they laugh, considering what they're planning to do to us?" Leah said, once more joining her son at the door.

"All the new faces seem unfamiliar somehow," Auntie Beattie sighed.

"Beattie! Shut up. And keep your eye on the till," Leah snapped. Then gazing at her son, lovingly, she shook her head to show that he just did not know the realities of the street. "Faces unfamiliar?" she ridiculed. "Only too familiar!"

"I do not understand you, Mother."

"With their eyes they don't need hands."

His eyelids flickered for a while and instead of speaking he nodded his head slowly.

"You're old enough, Aubrey, to face life, if you don't mind me saying so." Beattie held her mouth, hoping she had not spoken indiscreetly.

"They never leave a woman alone. Even me. And I'm not that young, am I? Mind you, I'm not that old. Am I?" No one confirmed or denied.

"Well, do you think I'm so decrepit that I still can't even be insulted? Sexually?"

Sister and son shook and nodded their heads so as not to make any mistake.

"What exactly do they want from me?" Leah asked all her ancestors in the sky.

"Well, it certainly ain't your intellectual equipment." Auntie Beattie laughed like a fishwife, and Aubrey was not surprised considering she used to sell herrings down Wentworth Street before her voracious appetite for a husband overcame her insatiable hunger for salted fish.

"A woman ain't safe in the streets nowadays," Auntie Beattie cooed.

"I should think you'd be perfectly safe, Auntie Beattie," he mumbled.

"So why didn't you stay on holiday?" Auntie Beattie slowly rolled her tongue over her cemetery of false teeth to extract loitering strands of chicken flesh.

"Aubrey pined for home. He cried bitterly for his bed. He got homesick, even after two days." He heard his mother spinning her traditional yarn, but he simply refused to look upon her face.

"Liar, I begged to stay and watch the wrath of the sea."

"You were such a lovely boy, Aubrey. Where did you go? I treat you like an eminent barrister, and you expect to be treated like... the Queen's physician."

He pressed his face against the glass of the window. A child poked out its yellow tongue as it passed.

81

Aubrey could see the sisters reflected in the glass as they moved about moaning and clutching various sections of their bodies.

Why on earth were they still on earth? Why were they still wound up? Two dried-up pieces of leather like Auntie Beattie and Leah the Feld would have looked rather charming in a nice glass case in the British Museum.

There was something definitely not nice about the old. Especially those who refused to move with the herd. Why had they refused to join that second most famous exodus in history — from Whitechapel to Golders Green? Why had they remained in the East End, which was now taken over by other scapegoats? Where was the treasure once buried along these streets?

"Where have all the Yidden gone? Long time passing. Where have all the Yidden gone, long time ago? Where have all the Yidden gone? Gone to Brent or Cricklewood —" His voice trailed off. One simply could not be ironic in Hessel Street.

"All right. There's the door, darling. You can get on a District Line train at Aldgate East. And if you change onto the Northern Line at Charing Cross, a train goes direct to Brent, Hendon and even to Edgware. Got your fare?" Leah smiled and opened her purse.

She survived by not moving. Like a fossil she soon became indistinguishable from the slums which had calcified around her. Every other Jew with self-respect had emigrated to North-West London, America, Israel, or the cemetery.

"Aubrey! You need a sleep." She was always a good judge of people in extremis, so he gladly re-entered the living room. "Don't hate me, Aubrey. I'm all you got," Leah shouted after him.

"I want to do well. All the family did well. They died for instance," he shouted back.

Aubrey slumped into his armchair and breathed in blissfully. This was the only item of furniture that he would not burn when the Plague hit London again. He savoured the smell of pre-Hitler upholstery and he felt good.

Yes. The Felds were all gone and the Newmans were gone.

The future of the whole overstrung tribe lay in his unemployed scrotum. Dead and gone, all of them. Gone into the wooden overcoat or the mink overcoat. Either way they were pretty rich and pretty high however low they had sunk. But whichever way you looked at it, they had all lost touch.

Everyone had gone and every white face had been replaced by a black face in Hessel Street. "Maybe that's what happens when you die. You come up again through a coal-hole all black in the face," he said to no-one.

Aubrey thought of his father, which caused tears to congregate in his eyes. He did not stop them rolling down his face. Besides, they tasted rather special.

Then he thought of all the girls he once knew. Beautiful and succulent and moaning. Gone were the stinkfinger girls of yesteryear. Girls waving goodbye, with hands and titties wobbling out of train windows. Girls smelling of delicious sweat and cheap scent. Where were they, with their pre-deodorant pussies?

And where were the smells of Hessel Street? And the new *cholas* being baked for sabbath and the barrels of cucumbers being pickled? And *lokshen* soup and old prayer books?

"Mind you, I wouldn't say no to a girl with a deodorant-saturated pussy at this moment," he remarked to the pale photo of his mother's grandmother, who never stopped watching him.

He knew that his last remaining link with the past had gone. The smell of his mother's delicious chicken soup had been cancelled out by the smell of curry. And that eternal Pakistani opera poured through the walls of the house next door, sounding like a chorus of cats having a collective breakdown.

"Curry is not enough. They have to send us culture." It was just as well that Jews were a patient and tolerant people. He took up the broom and pounded the wall with the wooden end. "Shut up that racket in there," he shouted.

Leah came into the dark living-room and dusted the wax tiger-lilies. "They've just offered money for the house — five thousand pounds cash. They even said they'd buy the business. Turn it into a Pakistani cakeshop. They can't wait for me to die so that they can fill every floor with sacks of rice and crates of instant cousins. On top of that they make it impossible for me to refuse by offering such good money."

"So what did you do?" He spoke slowly, his eyes closed.

"I refused."

She returned quickly to the counter. It was the place where she felt safest of all in the whole world of Whitechapel, but first she kissed Aubrey on the forehead. "I love you without a beard. Don't grow one. Look what happened to Bluebeard."

83

He watched her float away, and then within his closed eyes he saw another face. The face of his father. First, in medium long shot; then cleverly zooming to a close-up for a benign, smiling love scene, which naturally was devoid of any suggestion of incest.

There was no doubt his father and he shared the same profile and the same dream; the dream to escape Leah Feld, considerate and lovable as she was. It was obvious there was nothing personal in his desire to free himself of his dear and only mother. Life was an intricate little pattern of paradoxes. Those you loathed you could live with forever. Those you loved were the cause of eternal pain. That sort of love had to be terminated with ruthless, selfless courage.

The curried air closed around him, but despite his despair Aubrey felt very happy. This inconsistency did not distress him; not in the slightest. Humans were made of far more complex material than even the Great Tailor cared to recognise.

* * *

She was shaking him. He jumped up. He didn't know where he was. "What? Why you waking me? Was having such a nice dream." He pulled the blankets right over his head and curled up, but that didn't stop her. He knew she was still there.

"You were moaning. I heard you downstairs."

Aubrey threw the bedclothes off, then realised he was in his own room, upstairs. And he didn't know if it was night or day, or even what day it was.

"What day is it?"

"What do you mean, what day is it?"

"Why do you always answer questions with questions?"

"Me? Since when? So tell me why were you moaning?"

"What you talking about? I couldn't have been! I was dreaming of my father. Is it morning or night or just one of those days?"

He could tell she was about to perform. "When they buried him, they buried not a man but an archangel." Then she came back up to earth. "Aubrey —" he looked extremely pained "if only you took after me instead of your father."

He turned over to stare at the more relaxing wall. It didn't matter what day it was. Any day was every day, and every day was hopeless.

"What's the time?"

"What's so important about time suddenly? Catching an airship to Miami? Come down. The clock ticks down there."

He got out of bed and put on his pyjamas. But of course his mother had already left the room and was now mouching about the landing, thinking about prices wholesale and retail.

Aubrey always slept in his shirt and in his socks. After all, one never knew when the four minute warning would come. One could hardly be expected to rush to the underground station with bare toes.

But for decency's sake he always put on his pyjamas to go downstairs. He did not fancy presenting his aunt with new problems. In the first place Auntie Beattie was only human and overstrung. He did not wish to add to her burdens with thoughts of incest. One simply did not know what she would do next; and in the second place, people far less sexually demented than Auntie Beattie has succumbed to the coils of unnatural passion.

"What you don't have you don't miss." He poked out his tongue at the horrible yellow thing that darted in and out of his reflection's mouth.

He followed his mother on to the landing where she smiled at him. She smelled of mothballs and lavender and she stared with a slight smile poised tentatively upon her face.

"What you staring at, Mother?" He held her arm lightly, not wanting to be reminded of her surface frailty. She was a deep woman, full of symbolism.

"Just a fly that should have been hit with a rolled copy of *The Times* days ago." He clutched her bone with determination, and her enigmatic expression fell off.

"The Pakistanis will be signalling their Mosque in Woking before you know it, and we'll be occupied, and have to teach them English. And how to eat sweets."

Aubrey could see her proper mood. Leah did this performance at least once a year. No one knew the exact cause. "If we still don't understand the lemmings, how on earth can we possibly understand you, Mother?"

"I sacrificed everything for you, Aubrey. Because I loved your father. I must have been crazy, and everyone told me I was, because he was no good, but I wasn't mad, so I entered into negotiations, which were eventually engrossed. So we signed our lives away. And you came. And you were enough. With you and your father I think I did my duty. He never came down to earth. To turf, yes! But to earth no."

"I know, Mother. Men are curiously planned."

They both entered into the gloom of the living room.

"Let's go away, Mother. I mean somewhere further than Bournemouth. And let's stay longer than two days. I know, let's go to Calais?"

"You know I can't stand uncivilised places. Besides, the only way I'll leave this shop is in a box." She went out into the shop, smiling and nodding and shaking her head. "A mother is a mother," she said sadly.

He wondered if she was a secret Gertrude Stein or Anton Chekov reader. What on earth did she mean by her exit line?

Aubrey could not face the mirror nor the shock of the day, if it was day. For looking out of the window gave him no clue. The sky was neither here nor there. He *shlepped* up an old quilted bedspread, lowered himself and settled back into the armchair. The sounds of the sisters receded, and the sweetshop seemed to be far, far away.

But Leah returned, thrusting something towards him.

"Have a beigel. It's fresh and lovely and hot!" Then she faded back into the unreal distance again. He took the beigel, bit a chunk out of it and threw the rest away over his shoulder.

He would not succumb to the temptations of his young days, when he used beigels rather than doughnuts under the sheets. They were somehow more proper and less messy. However, even doughnuts, fresh or stale, were preferable to using the hand. For that method was unmistakably self abuse, and therefore reprehensible. Besides, even beigels had been redundant for a long time, owing to the never ceasing growth of his now magnificent Goliath.

He had merely outgrown all that, but just this once he decided to resort to his right hand and pray later. He pulled his hot companion ever so gently, thinking of various women and projecting them onto the screen of his mind.

First of all the intelligent nude who had adorned the cover of the intellectual Sunday supplement. But she didn't work, so he rejected her and conjured up Rita Cohen, a girl he had once been rather intimate with. Yes, he remembered well those mad days when he played hospitals with Rita. On his sixth birthday she allowed him three fanny probes with his little finger and he never saw her again. A recent eye-witness told him that she worked for a hairdresser in Cricklewood and was still something sensational if you looked close.

But Rita as she once was also wouldn't work the magic, and Goliath still showed no signs of getting up. He pictured film stars, lady politicians and even a few left-wing lady novelists. But nothing seemed to work, so he put it away, and tried to think about other things.

He loved the old armchair even though the leather was torn and it was falling to pieces. He rubbed his nose into its guts.

The smell of the leather and the straw interior was the smell of the past, the smell of his smell, the sweet tobacco smell of his father. It was the smell of security, of dark, lingering safety.

Often he had turned this armchair upside down, to hide beneath it, to hear them speak of him.

"That boy will be the death of me," Leah in the past said again and again. "The death of me. The death of me."

"*Aluvi*! You can do with a rest," he replied ever so gently.

Where did statements go, once they had been uttered? He wondered for a moment, then came up with the answer. They didn't go anywhere; they lingered for certain sensitive souls to pull them down from the dark ceiling stains in order to play them back once again.

"That boy is so gifted," his father said. "Why does my son turn out to be exceptional?"

Father was getting into his uniform. He was going off to Russia this very evening, to organise the Red Army for Trotsky.

"Naturally, Trotsky will get all the credit." Father was tugging his tight, long leather boots on to his rather splendid feet. Only boots of such obvious calibre were worthy to walk the Siberian winter.

"That boy will drive me to the grave," his mother cried, stirring and stirring the soup, adding garlic and tears.

"Aubrey is exceptional. He will go far." And these were the last words his father uttered before he left the house, resplendent in his cavalry regalia. "Aubrey will go far," he repeated loudly from the street he was already striding through.

"Not far enough," Leah replied. She didn't look down the street as neighbours came out to cheer his receding father who was going just as he came, stars in his eyes — the red star of Karl Marx in the left eye and the golden star of King David in his right eye. Everyone threw red, white and blue streamers and confetti as they softly hummed the *Internationale*.

But Leah did not leave the scullery. She cried all the time into the food she was always preparing.

He never saw his father again. And even if he had died before Kiev, who was he, Aubrey Field, to stand in judgment of a hero of such stature? Anyway, his father was dead. Aubrey was sure. Solomon Feld was the dying sort. People with one golden eye and one crimson eye always were.

And Leah cried six or eight tears into the soup every day; you had to give credit where it was due. It was extremely unkind of him to believe she was merely trying to save a pinch of salt.

He could hear them squabbling again in the shop. Auntie Beattie and his mother were having an intense love affair. Arguments were their sole means of contact. The sisters needed each other's curses as other people needed a kind act and an encouraging word.

Aubrey turned the armchair upside down and managed to get under it without too much strain or overlap.

He knew he was not as lithe and bendable as he once was. You had to watch yourself, even if you had barely entered your thirties. His mind sauntered back to a few years before this day.

It was probably 1941, and he was about ten years old or eleven. He remembered it distinctly. But then again why shouldn't he? Wasn't it only the other day when the sirens wailed and the bombs crumped and mortals descended into the underground? Every night they had to shelter beneath the streets of the city and Aubrey loved it.

"Why me? Why do they want me dead?" Leah cried skyward every time the earth trembled. "What did I do to them?"

One simply could not tell her that it was not the direct wrath of Hitler and Goering that caused them to live in this deep-down world of carbolic and common humanity.

"Aubrey! He's got it in for us. Specially you and me," she said, smoke curling up from her red-stained fag-end. "Each bomb's engraved with your name and my name: Aubrey and Leah Feld." She licked her finger and drew their names in the dust of the platform. "That's why you mustn't let one single bomb on us. We mustn't give that monster satisfaction. Understand?" She shook his little limp arm. "Understand?"

"No, Mother." Then his eyes would close and he would sleep,

all curled up on the noisy underground platform. It was beautiful beneath the soles of feet, the cemeteries, the worms and the roots of trees and all those crouching creatures who watched and waited, peeping up through grass or paving stones or floorboards and lino, ready to spring on their two hairy legs.

But he grew out of his socks, and the all-clear sounded. And time passed. Sometimes it passed right out, and sprawled out on the floor in front of you. But it passed. As sure as other people's lives. Time passed and passed.

"The monster didn't get us." Leah giggled as Aubrey waltzed her down Hessel Street on VE day.

They danced and danced, and the war was over. "Wonder why he never managed to burn us into clouds?" Jewish women of her sort had a special way of staring at the sky. They always seemed to be saying, "I've taken enough from you." Even though they sort of smiled. But she soon contributed a normal, non-Jewish smile, and even drank some Christian beer.

Later, with a slow solemn glide, she went along the street, doling out lollipops and bags of sweets and packets of Sir Walter Raleigh Coconut Tobacco to the thousands and thousands of hands and mouths turned upward and open towards her.

Later that day all London danced. And then they were all gone, the faces, the songs and the bunting. But Aubrey could not sleep so she took him to Victoria Park, which was totally deserted except for ducks.

By the lake she stood, and by the lake she cried. And by the lake he stood like a *shlemiel*, watching the sky lit up from all the fireworks and fires of joy. And no longer did he hear the blood-curdling call of the sirens, and he hardly ever travelled on the underground. But those tube trains came back sometimes like roaring red dragons, hurtling through his dreams, crashing towards him with innards full of green people.

Leah spoke, and he shot up. His thumping heart had missed a beat, but she was merely talking to herself in the shop; checking and rechecking the stock, jotting down instructions to herself. "Don't forget, Leah — running low on sherbet dabs and refreshers."

Aubrey laughed so that she could hear.

"You can laugh. The secret of selling is buying."

Aubrey laughed again. He felt so warm and beautiful.

"You can laugh. You'll never hear truer words. That reminds

me. Aubrey! Phone Beehive tomorrow. We're running low on nougat." But he didn't respond. "All right! Don't. If we run out of nougat you'll suffer. It's your legacy that will go down the drain." Leah shouted with glee. Then she continued checking.

It was as if she expected the entire stock to be whisked away when she turned her back. She didn't trust the goods. As soon as she turned away, she'd turn right back again and start recounting until a customer came.

Some little girls were giggling somewhere, and reminded him of the children who once played upon these pavements.

All baggy they were, as if wearing cast-off adults' rags that had been stuffed with newspapers and sawdust.

In those days streets were full of kids shouting and laughing and flirting and teasing and crying. How he envied them when he pressed his face against the glass! He wanted so much to join their games of Old Tin Can and Knocking Down Ginger.

"Go out and play," Leah nagged as usual for she could never see that they were too rough.

"They want me for sweets! They think I'll pinch some for them. Don't want to play."

"Go. Go out and play." He could still hear her nagging as she pushed him to the door. He could still hear himself sobbing.

She ought to have understood that he was far too fragile for them. And sensitive. It was before the war, after all. And in 1938 he could only have been three or four years old. Aubrey opened one eye, and looked at his mother, who was quickly fanning her flushed face, employing every single finger. Why did she always maintain he was thirty-eight years old, or thirty-nine? What on earth possessed her to insist that he had been born in 1930?

He closed his eyes again and went back into the deep dark.

"True, I might even be a little bit older than thirty-two or three, or even four. But thirty-eight is ridiculous!" he reassured himself, silently, and felt better.

But in the darkness he could no longer conjure up those pre-cathode children. He could just about imagine the lamppost where they used to swing around and around on a skipping rope.

But those children were gone. Gone forever. They hadn't even left a ghost behind.

There were plenty of ghost people. Adult ghosts were ten a penny in Whitechapel. Asthmatic, wheezing ghosts on crutches, sighing as they came towards you — smiling painfully, begging with their eyes for a little bit of sympathy as they walked right through you shuddering, leaving you all damp and heavy and limp with the water from their eyes and the vapour from their sighs.

He would even have tolerated ghost children walking through the shutters of the shop and pinching acid drops or a half pound box of milk chocolates.

But now there was no one. Just the sisters and himself, and not a living person in the shop.

He decided that he would have to make do with the lone pink image of that lovely living boy — himself, as he was before the war, when he was either three, or five, or eight. What did it matter? Nothing mattered now, for there was the lovely laughing boy that he was, tight curls smothering his head, eating a chocolate eclair, waving to him from a tram or bus or tube-train.

"Lo, Aubrey. How are you, son?" he cried, waving back at the child.

"I'm lovely, Aubrey. How are you?"

"Incredibly splendid, Aubrey. Goodbye, Aubrey. Don't get lost and worry your mother."

"Bye Aubrey! Lovely seeing you. Love to you and to all of you."

"Goodbye — Aubrey —"

And the sirens wailed again. The wolves of war were snarling at the door.

* * *

The wind howled across the river. It obviously did not observe the Sabbath of the Christian god.

Then it occurred to Aubrey. It was a Jewish wind and had taken the day off yesterday. Now it howled and howled, but sometimes it sighed. Yes! It was definitely a Jewish wind.

"Loan us half a crown, Mrs Spiegelhalter. Lend us half a crown." It howled.

"Mr Levine, I want you. Mr Levine, have I got a bone to pick with you?" Many bones had been picked. Millions of bones of the Jewish dead. Natural or otherwise. In Whitechapel natural. Elsewhere unnatural. All the bones had been sifted and graded and rendered down. All the bones except his own, his mother's, and Auntie Beattie's.

"Believe me, have I got a pain in my back!" the wind now

groaned. Was he awake or asleep? Or was he dreaming he was awake? What did it matter?

Even the barges complaining in the fog were worm-eaten tailors who once huddled together outside Black Lion Yard discussing bladder trouble, unemployment and Karl Marx. And seagulls shrieking over the Pool of London were aunts calling from windows in the sky; calling Dave and Shirley and Doris home to plates of egg and chips.

All dead. All were dead. All the Jews were dead. All the Jewish dead were wailing together, and making no bones about it.

"Must get away," he heard himself say, "from this Whitechapel burial ground."

The Jews did die here, one way or another. The spirit died. They came here to live and feed their young but still felt far away from nowhere they could name. And here they waited, beside the waters of nowhere. They hung their singing children up to dry, worked and slaved, huddled together in a great herd, developed thick hides, and sacrificed. Then they died exhausted, hunted and haunted.

And now they were gone. "The elephant and the Jewish problem." He stuffed four strips of spearmint into his mouth, chewed them together and laughed.

There was no more Jewish problem. There were no more Jews.

"Hitler won the war! Hitler won the war!" The melancholic aunt-gulls shrieked high and low, but in chorus.

"Lend us half a crown! Pay you back, *Shobbus*." The contralto wind sighed deeply. "Mrs Spiegelhalter! Please spare me half a crown."

"Mr Levine! I want you. Have I got a bone to pick with you." The fat Yiddisher now soprano breeze fluttered over all other sounds rising from the earth.

In the other room, outside his dream, the till added its own funeral tones, each coin adding another farewell note to his own lost lostness. Until —

Aubrey was young again. Belly gone. His face no higher than the table-top, his head of hair a barber's nightmare.

The streets were full, because people came out of their houses in those days. He was being led away by the Indian toffee-man who was taking him to India, where they would both live on Indian toffee. Day and all night for evermore.

"Why you taking me away?" Aubrey asked the ever-smiling milk-chocolate face that conjured perfumed pear drops from eyes and mouth.

"I want whole of Asia to see how nice boy you are," the man said, spinning more and more strands of sky blue pink sugar, and whisking fountains and fountains of Indian candy floss from his nostrils which floated straight into the gaping wide mouth of child Aubrey beside him.

Then he heard his mother call the dark down, so the Indian toffee-man ran away, across the road, barefoot, carrying his shoes. He was soon lost in the crowd, and he was never seen again.

So Aubrey turned to his father striding along with heroic moustache and visionary look in eyes. Solomon Feld walked right down Mile End Road, applauded by all the tailors and furriers who continued arguing as soon as he passed.

Father marched straight to Aldgate East underground station and asked the booking clerk for a ticket to Kiev, where he had a pre-arranged meeting with Leon Trotsky and thereby he saved Russia from those reactionary hordes who attacked a few weeks later.

Aubrey waved at his father outside the kosher slaughter-house, and his father waved back. Unemotionally; with his usual economy of movement, nobility of stance and dignity of expression.

When his mother dragged him all the way back to Hessel Street he was crying, for his father exploded in a sky bursting with streamers and candy floss. "Never go with foreigners. He'll turn you into Indian toffee, take you back to Hong Kong and pass you off as a darkie. They can even uncircumcise boys, so I heard. Don't wander off again."

"But Mother, it was Father, I had to say goodbye. All Russia was waiting for him."

He knew he was still dreaming, so he didn't crouch down when the synagogue exploded in Stepney Green. The debris made no sound as the shattered building fell all around him.

Families stood around roasting meat and chestnuts in the flames, but the *chazen* didn't seem to notice as he stood before the broken Ark, raising his silver goblet overflowing with the Palestinian wine, pitching his voice to the sky which was God's last known address.

Aubrey left the desolation and followed his mother past the Jewish hospital, where sad faces of dead children peered from every window. Little hands waved slowly down at him. He waved back and he blew a bubble especially for them from his everlasting strip of bubblegum. The bubble became so enormous that it filled the whole of Stepney Green and reached almost as high as the fingertips of the dead children. They laughed and laughed silently behind the glass.

Then he caught another glimpse of his father, galloping in the opposite direction. But he could not quite see the horse. His father's moustache was so grand now that surely God would be jealous and therefore claim him before the racing season ended. One day the wings of that moustache would rotate and Solomon Feld would soar up into the evening sky.

"Yes! Look! There he goes. He's waving down at us, Mother."

"I'm going to join Trotsky, to show him how to organise the Red Army," Father called down through a megaphone, but soon he was no more than a speck in the ever-congealing sky.

"Bring him back! Bring him back!" Aubrey called, but the Almighty was as jealous as the next man, or used earplugs. Either way Aubrey was most reluctant to blame God. There were terrible sounds around in those days. And shortages. "Are there soup kitchens in heaven, Mother?"

But his mother pulled him away from the shivering street and he never ever saw his father again. Except like now, in dreams.

Outside the school in Senrab Street he stood with her. The huge pram crammed with sweets that she was selling to the baggy children.

And as he spoke, confectionery still rained down: bull's eyes, toffee apples, gobstoppers, chocolate kisses, lucky bags, liquorice whirls. And children were rushing everywhere, thousands of thin little white faces sucking, sucking, their clothes bulging with their surplus, which fell down their sleeves continuously and littered the whole of Mile End Waste.

Later Leah pushed the pram home.

"Maybe I need a brother in that pram, more than bull's eyes!"

"You're too beautiful to be repeated!" she replied.

"Aubrey, Aubrey," the children mocked.

"Aubrey! Aubrey! Fat little Aubrey. He's got silk *gutkers* on, and money in his pocket."

"Maybe, but my father and Trotsky are conspiring to change the world."

"Don't you ever have anything to do with Trotsky," she said briskly, pushing the pram onward. "You're better off without him."

He cried. She patted his head. "If only you weren't so innocent. So beautiful."

"Can you loan me half a crown?" the Yiddisher wind howled. Then it, too, curled up and died of cold. And the elements made no more sound.

"Oh Father, who art in Russia, send me back your medals, or a photo of your grave," he prayed.

He remembered how she screamed in Yiddish on that day, "A *broch* on his *kishkers*." He never discovered if she had meant God, his father, or himself.

"Why do you cry when you curse?"

"To me, Yiddish is a holy language, too touching to speak," she replied, dabbing her eyes. Leah was taking him home from school. It was the first time he had gone amongst the barbarians. He cried and hated it and licked his bleeding knees, but soon she was taking him to and from school all the time.

Then he was going there all on his own.

He looked at his teacher. She wore tortoiseshell glasses and did not smile behind them. She just looked right through you.

It was November 28th, just after school had ended. They were alone on the stairs, Miss Levy and himself. Every detail was crystal clear.

"'You have the gift, Aubrey. You are touched by the gods, Aubrey. You can do anything, Aubrey. Anything. Any time. You will go far, Aubrey. You can go far, Aubrey. You should go far, Aubrey. Perhaps I'll give you private tuition, Aubrey. Come to my house, any evening you like, I can fit you in. Come."

Miss Levy was very nice, even if she did breathe heavily down her nose. Her face was close, desiring him.

He never went to her house. Maybe he should have been kind and given her the thing she most urgently required. After all, good deeds never went amiss. He had so much to give, so much to spare. But he decided against Miss Levy. He had no wish to hurt her. But what was the point in giving her a solitary glimpse of paradise if he merely had to withdraw it again? It was better for her to languish in her dark cell of hopeful frustration.

Anyway, he had nothing to spare for her.

Leah turned her pram into a tuckshop and his father was a dead hero. But none of the kids believed the amazing exploits of his fabulous father. They even had the audacity to demand photographic proof. So he washed his hands and the past disappeared like dirt.

Aubrey opened each eye separately, and returned into the frozen curried air of reality. But he experienced no overwhelming desire to stand upright, so he slowly moved about on all fours, imagining that he was a lizard born before the beginning of time, before the invention of human eyes.

Then he got up and stretched and yawned. And yawned.

A wonderful thing had happened while he had been replaying his tapes of personal history: Auntie Beattie had gone home. He looked out at the violent purple sky. He longed for a miracle. Perhaps he would see his *luftmensch* father today.

He loved miracles, because they were few and far between. Infrequent beacons that threw light upon the darkness of the world, reminding people that people were not nice, and that goodness and justice did not prevail. It was always reassuring to face the prevailing darkness with such concrete faith.

In the empty shop his darling mother leaned over the till.

"Where would I be without her?" he asked himself.

"Nowhere," he replied.

He owed everything to this unique and beautiful lady who stood in his way only because she thought she might be right. Certainly he felt qualms and regret for what he was about to do, but he decided that he could not replace the breadknife. He would walk straight towards her and cut her throat; thus he would take away all her financial worries and all those interminable forms she had to fill in. No longer would she have to argue with that sadistic accountant who almost made her spit blood.

He held the breadknife behind his back and journeyed the endless distance of twenty feet, to where Leah was bent in financial anguish. An old woman, especially his own mother, should not have to cope with such gigantic problems, not to mention such a problematic son like himself.

He stood right behind her. "You're worried, Mother. Poor Mother."

"Worried! Course I'm worried."

Never had there been so much compassion in his voice. "It's me, isn't it? I wouldn't wish myself upon anyone."

She turned but did not see the knife. "I'm worried about money," she said.

She was such a marvellous woman. She never once complained of the rheumatism which coursed through her brave little body.

Nor could he remember Leah once mentioning her frightful fear of dying from cancer of everything.

He knew she had to have both the pains and the fears. Those surely were the occupational diseases of mothers who lived beyond their term, not out of personal consideration but for the sake of exceptional siblings, who could not conform easily like the rest of the dross.

He felt very, very close to her. Already all his trivial, negative feelings were falling away. Only the best of her would survive with him.

"You're not worried about money," he replied.

"Who worries about money?" she ridiculed.

"Only those with it and those without it."

He would cut her throat beautifully. One straight stroke. Swift and deep. A kosher killing by a devoted son.

"Wasn't it Oscar Wilde, or Sholom Aleichem, who once put it so succinctly? 'The coward does it with a kiss, the brave man with a sword.'"

Leah seemed shocked. "Oscar Wilde! Please don't mention that name in this house."

"He was also human."

"Human? A man who leaves his wife and children you call human?" She slapped her face and nodded. "What you babbling about, Aubrey? You look funny." Then flickering her fingers, she indicated he should bend at the knees, just a little bit.

Aubrey complied and Leah felt his forehead. Then she smiled joyfully and turned away again.

Clutching the knife tightly again he prepared himself for the one final thrust. Yet still the voice of hopeless reason wanted to be heard. How could he stop it? Deep down he was as human as every other stupid person. But he decided to indulge his one strand of cowardly weakness, his one final last throw.

"Mother! One last question —"

"Last? Why last? You decided to be happy for a change?"

"Mother, you must let me go. I love you, cherish you and respect you. But I must have my freedom."

"Darling! One thing makes me different from other mothers: I don't particularly enjoy being one. Go. Now. And report sometimes. Look! Here's fifty."

She opened the till, "Well, anyway, here's fifteen pounds and seven pence ha'penny. Leave. It's time you left. You'll be happier and I'll be happier. We'll get on so nice when you're not here."

She was an amazing actress; this performance could have convinced the whole world. Only he could see through the subtlety of the act. If he so much as took one step into that foggy street, she would collapse into an emotional moaning heap. And she would never forgive him, and he would never forgive himself. "If I left, you'd never get over what you thought was heartlessness."

"Try me and see, darling." She opened the door and the non-paying fog entered the premises. Then she hobbled away mumbling, "Sacrifice! For why? Ain't I a person in my own right?" Leah appealed to the news announcer on the television screen. "Only the other day they were talking about women and what they are, apart from the usual thing, in the House of Commons. We're also people, believe it or not. Go, Aubrey! I don't expect no reward. My reward is you going. I brought you up. You're up now, and you can walk. So — toodleoo."

He held the knife high above the back of her neck whilst a vision of Valentino came to him.

He would simply drag her back, rather gently, and pinion her to the floor by using soothing, firm pressure. But no force. Then, with utmost compassion and perhaps a few last words of respect, he would pull the breadknife sharply across the whole length of her soft neck.

"What you doing with that knife, Aub?" Auntie Beattie's voice hit him like a fistful of jagged stars. "You might have an accident. Knives attract lightning."

It *was* Auntie Beattie behind him. He could have sworn she had gone home.

And Leah turned round as he lowered the knife-edge. "Mother! I must have more money. You must raise my allowance. Look at me! I'm a *shloch*. I can't exist any more on handouts." He looked along the saw-like edge of the breadknife with expertise and calmness.

"But Aubrey! Darling! Your mother gives you everything. Her blood even, if you needed it. You don't want for nothing." The myopic eyes of Auntie Beattie were drowning in her predictable oceans, whose tides rose and fell, regularly and constantly. And he was furious. Anyone would think that he had not sacrificed almost his whole youth for his mother. Anyone would believe that he had treated his mother without respect and consideration.

"Shut up, Auntie! This is between my mother and myself." Now they would see he meant business.

Auntie Beattie's lip quivered and her voice became even more hysterical. "Why's he so touchy? What have I done to him? This a way to treat an aunt? An aunt like me, especially? Why's he so touchy, Leah?"

"Touchy? You telling me something? He's so sensitive these days you have to speak to him through a silk handkerchief."

Auntie Beattie went towards her sister, closer to the source of her solace, but Leah stepped back, sharply. "But Aubrey's right. It's nothing to do with you, Beattie. Stop interfering."

Auntie Beattie forgot she was in the middle of a fit of weeping hysteria and retreated into a corner where she slumped into the rickety wicker chair and gazed at them with her pale open and shut face. "You're my only family, and this is how you treat me," she said quietly through the fingers that covered her astonished mouth.

Aubrey faced Leah, head on. Now she would see the determined fire in his eyes. Now she would realise that no power on earth could thwart him.

"Well, Mother? I'm waiting for you to agree with me."

"No," she said.

"No? Why not?" he pleaded. "What are you saving it for?"

"For a rainy day." Leah pushed a choc-ice into her mouth. Then, remembering her rudeness, she took it out again and thrust it towards him. "Choc-ice? Go on. It's lovely."

The choc-ice touched the tip of his nose before he shook his head with dignified rage.

"She's saving up for a rainy day," Auntie Beattie repeated. At times like this she became a toneless echo of her older sister.

"A rainy day!" Aubrey shouted back with all the sarcasm he could muster. Then he threw the street door open. It was raining cats and dogs outside. In fact, it was one of the rainiest days he had seen for a long time. "I must leave you then. Now! Forever! And for always!"

She applauded with lit-up eyes. "At last, Aubrey. You'll appreciate me. You'll thank me for making you make this decision. But don't come to thank me in person. Not often. Thank me on the phone, you can always reverse the charge."

"You're doing the right thing. Thank God."

He had every intention of leaving that very moment, but the rain was very wet. But he would go. Without any doubt he would be gone as soon as the worst of the deluge was over.

He slammed the door shut. "You think you're being subtle. You think you have me for always. But I shall show you." He faced the face that had held him in bondage since the beginning of time. "You've always tried to take advantage of my better nature."

"Sometimes it's just as well," she remarked sadly, as she tried to release the breadknife from his grasp.

He returned to the living room and put the knife beside the loaf of baked sawdust. Then he peered out of the fly-blown window, out at the steaming streets and pelting sky.

"I'm going to bed; for the rest of the day." His voice sliced through the air and he stamped all the way up the stairs.

He got into bed, but despite his loneliness his right hand could always be relied on to keep him company. So he held his own willing flesh. "A friend in need is a friend indeed."

* * *

Aubrey had watched too many dawns to indulge in the false luxury of hope. Night was somebody else's awful day on the other side of the world, and darkness was merely a device to separate one monotonous day from another.

And now a new day had arrived with predictable punctuality, but nothing new would happen. No one would come to surprise him, and yesterday would be exactly duplicated. Consequently, he did not react ecstatically when the first fingers of dawn stroked the dark hairy belly of the world.

But all was not despair. Something new could possibly happen this day. Perhaps he would be able to kill himself just after breakfast; spectacularly, by diving off London Bridge. Or by kebabing himself in front of an Inner Circle train, at the height of the morning rush hour. "All is not lost, my boy."

But his optimism proved short-lived. Someone or other would be bound to rescue him just in time. For some incredible reason society could not abide you suiciding yourself. It was probably sheer jealousy. "We've got to suffer this miserable existence; why should you escape?" they were saying.

He descended towards the monologues of the two sisters who appeared to be talking to each other. A stranger could be excused if he thought that they were engaged in an involved conversation.

There was no point in prevaricating any longer. The rain had stopped and today was as good as any other day for chopping down the family tree. He put on his scarf and overcoat and decided to take a one way ticket to eternity immediately. Aubrey was about to leave the house and enter Hessel Street.

"Where you going this time of day? Without even breakfast?" Leah raced him to the street door and stood with her back against it.

"I'm going to kill myself," he replied with the sort of emotion people usually reserved for ordering poached eggs on toast. She looked terribly concerned and he was glad. At last she was realising that he was a man of his word.

"Kill yourself? Aubrey! Did I hear right?" Her voice went up and up. "Aubrey! That's no way to leave home."

Auntie Beattie joined them. She smiled more than usual and smelled of lavender and paraffin. Auntie Beattie varied her smell almost every day. "Ah, don't give us that. He's off to a rendez-vous. With a girl." She nudged her sister, "I told you, Leah. He's a dark horse." Her continuing nudges seemed unnecessarily forceful.

"I wish it was a girl. I'm not the sort of woman who thinks no girl's good enough for my boy. I'd pity any girl."

He watched his mother for a moment. This would be the very last time he would see her alive. "I am going to end it all," he said very slowly.

"Whatever you do, at least eat some breakfast. You can't do anything proper on an empty stomach. It's not nice." She scooted into the kitchen and returned with a pickled cucumber speared on a fork. She smiled contentedly as she watched him munch the offering.

"Leah! Whatever happened to that nice girl Aubrey took out

once or twice? Every time they looked at each other I heard the school choir sing Psalm 150. And I could almost taste the marzipan on such a gigantic wedding cake."

"Beattie, pipe down." Leah tried not to shout.

He felt quite sorry for Auntie Beattie, even if she was a stupid, silly, interfering old cow.

"You remember, Aub. What was her name again? No, don't tell me. I remember —"

"Please shut up, Beattie," Leah hissed through clenched teeth. But Beattie, for once in a while, took no notice.

"Wait! She was a well-built, lovely girl. On the tip of the tongue. Yes! I know! Wait! It was Miriam. Miriam Smythe. Aub, what happened to her?"

Aubrey opened the door. "Oh, her! She petered out before she petered in. So long, you two. See you if we end up in the same place." The ladies sensed there was nothing else to say, and no one broke the silence as he left the house, and entered the street for his last exit.

"Aubrey! Aubrey! I must tell you something." It was her voice calling him. He turned and grinned.

Her face alone had entered the cold world of Whitechapel. There was no point in him not listening to her last words. All condemned people received and deserved this privilege. And God knows it would be hard enough on her, being condemned to live in a world without him.

So he waited. And while she blew her nose and cleared her throat he waited some more. He was in no hurry. The worms would simply have to queue up patiently.

"Aubrey! Here is my last word of advice. Come down to earth. I know it's nice to live in clouds and imagine you're something you ain't, but remember, people without money shouldn't go to auction sales. Understand? And listen to me, Aubrey, this is even more important. Never be ashamed of your origins and where you live. And always wrap up warm. Now you know everything, Aubrey. Go! Go now. I wish you luck."

He turned and walked away from the smiling face that oozed tears that fell and splashed upon the wet paving stones.

He was going far away from Hessel Street. He might have been born amongst these stones, but if there was the remotest chance of dying today, he certainly was not going to have his body lifted and fingered by the street sweepers of Tower Hamlets.

Yes, he would die with ease, for he had grown to maturity. He had reached that exceptional state of adulthood which few men achieve. All in all, he had nothing to complain about, even if that in itself was something to complain about.

He turned into Commercial Road, and sang in his usual sonorous voice, "Say goodbye to your airs and your graces, say goodbye to your pants and your braces, say goodbye to your birds and the races —"

Of course, there was still time to achieve mortal success, but what was the point? Everyone who knew him said he could go to Rome today and after a year return with his remarkably unique talent transmuted into one of the greatest baritone sounds in the whole of singing history.

Or why shouldn't he be able to take up the brush in Paris and astonish the whole art world, if he so cared? "Look at Gaugin and the breasts of his dusky maids." He spoke loudly for all the streets to hear and he certainly did not mind in the least when the two passing schoolgirls started giggling. If Paul Gaugin could pull it off, why not Aubrey Field?

And what about Vincent and Picasso, and Chagall? They too did not deny their compulsion despite their years. But what was the use? Who would appreciate him sacrificing a quiet life for the responsibilities of adulation? At least in the cosy, dark grave, no one nagged you to get up. You just slept in, doing nothing for ever and ever. And, best of all, you didn't have to be anything down there. Your mouldy clothes held no money or membership card to the Playboy Club, and your apologies for fingers held no steering wheel, no girl, no school diploma. Everyone was equal inside the grass door.

Yes, suicide still remained a distinct possibility. Anything was better than breathing and thinking and having to feel guilty about the misery of a sad, mad, sweet, and senile mother.

He walked towards Gardiner's Corner, passing street after street full of emptiness, past all the familiar dead faces that loomed Lazarus-like before him. Sometimes they waved from puddles, sometimes they cried in endless queues that stretched from the roadside right up into the low clouds.

And there were happy faces, bartering and bickering and arguing over philosophy, pogroms and pickled herrings. These faces contrasted sharply with the living masks perched on programmed bodies on their way to factories.

When he reached the junction he realised he was incredibly hungry. His mother was correct; it would never do to die on an empty stomach.

He could just see her at the autopsy as the coroner's words added insult to injury: "He had not partaken of any food that morning. And please, Madam, the beating of... ahem... breasts and the pulling of handfuls of hair isn't going to help anyone."

Aubrey thought of Oscar Wilde and his tribulations. And Aldgate East became the outer wall of a tyrannical prison, and the East End was the entire soulless world to which he had been despatched.

He had rarely gone beyond Aldgate East. Beyond here lay a world of infinite opportunity and he could not call to mind the last time he had dared to gaze upon the walls where freedom started. There had been no point.

He felt like conversation, but there was simply no-one he could talk to — not a single girl, not a solitary bus conductor, not even the not exactly plain female assistants at the public library. One in particular came to mind and would have sufficed, had she not a perpetual gust of halitosis below her glasses.

He sometimes did catch a glimpse of wild young girls when they crawled out from their depraved cellars behind the Whitechapel Art Gallery — girls who would fall instantly for his iconoclasm and complexity. And even if some did have dirty feet, he could easily accidentally push the goldfish bowl over them as they entered his house at three-thirty in the morning.

Anyway, what was the point of goldfish? You couldn't have a relationship with them.

His belly would not stop grumbling. And it became sheer ecstatic agony when his nostrils received a sudden whiff of fish. Fish frying. Silver Jewish fish. He was damned hungry for anything but goldfish.

Two giggling birds with legs right up to their bums passed by. He closed his eyes and breathed the smell of them in.

He knew that their conversation did not contain one single reference to Kant. But he saw no reason why he should not follow them, captivate them and seduce them; incredibly.

He could just see his mother foaming at the till when he had each in turn downstairs on the floor, and then upstairs. How could a son explain the new morality, when he and his friends practised such a very old, yet delectable habit?

It would just be too bad for his mother, she would simply have to have a heart attack or walk into the Thames if he did not oblige by his own exit. He would say, "Dear Mother, I have decided to cheat the worms. Meanwhile, we are all having each other, for one calendar month. And, incidentally, the goldfish is dead."

But these were daydreams, and therefore not nearly as real as nightmares. Consequently, his joy was short-lived. He knew he could never take anyone back there. His mother he could just about explain away. His background and occupation would be impossible to live down.

Aubrey had to admit the awful truth, he was ashamed of his origins. He was ashamed of the house and the sweetshop. He shuddered as he imagined himself explaining himself to the more fortunate inhabitants of the earth.

"My name is Aubrey Field, from Hessel Street and of Hessel Street. And I am just going home to weigh up four ounces of sugar babies because that happens to be my occupation. But between you and me, I munch five hundred jelly babies every day. I bite right through their belly-buttons."

He was ashamed — ashamed that his mother had never had the courage to move through the North-west passage for the far-flung acres of Brent and North Finchley. He was ashamed of not having a fast-moving red vehicle to carry him from nowhere in particular to nowhere in particular. He was ashamed that he wasn't a consultant or a barrister, or even an accountant or dentist. He was ashamed that he couldn't boast. And with all that shame, how could he possibly hope to impress anyone? So what was the purpose in continuing such a shameful existence?

Suicide seemed to be the only reasonable way out of his predicament. So he whistled, because he felt gay again.

"As my mother says, one door closes, another door closes." Aubrey laughed and he didn't care what lorry drivers thought.

And his feet were suddenly taking him to the only logical place under the circumstances.

The Kosher Wimpy Bar! In Middlesex Street. Aubrey entered the neon interior where two-legged animals were devouring four-legged animals with a ravenous stare and a chomping mouth. Their hands and arms all round their plates, protecting their kosher portion of cow. Their eyes darted to and fro just like the final day at Wimbledon.

"Oh, it's wrong, so wrong, to eat the flesh of a living creature. It's despicable and unforgivable, and if I were not killing myself I'd become vegetarian," Aubrey mumbled as he munched the delicious preparation before him. "Anyway, why should I go to God as a hypocrite? I shall face him with a blood-stained conscience, and I shall expect no mercy, and maybe be forwarded to hell where the truly wicked reside."

Besides, heaven was pointless. It would be even lonelier than Commercial Road on a Sunday afternoon. Only Auntie Beattie would be in heaven, even if she did fancy her own nephew. Aubrey was sure God was broad-minded.

"Do you have a delicious banana split?" he murmured suggestively to the frenzied woman who was mentally adding up figures behind the counter.

When he stopped enjoying the delights of his subtle mind, he watched four nibbling secretaries. He could just see them marching along Whitechapel High Street, returning to their offices, all of them smartly swinging along in precise military step. "Left titty! Right titty, left titty right titty. Cha-a-nge TITTY! Right titty! Left titty! Right titty! Present TITTIES!"

Then he started laughing until it became uncontrollable, so he had to clasp his hand tightly over his mouth.

They sent back nothing in return except waves of aphrodisiac from their exquisite oceans of lust.

And then he saw her. She sat three places along the counter opposite him, sipping lemon tea. The imprint of her mouth was stained on the rim of the tumbler.

He inched towards her, not caring if anyone thought he was one of those creatures who lived by the balls alone. Anyone in his right mind could tell at a glance that all he wanted was to gaze down her dress and try to glimpse the garnet bumps which surmounted her soft, pink domes. But the place was crammed so it was impossible to get close to her.

"Excuse me. My mother just died and she always sat in this chair. Do you mind?" His inclined head oozed two tears, just for the little Jewish penguin who sat beside him. Aubrey wanted everyone excluded from the temple that surrounded her.

The little man shuffled away, seeming relieved that it was not his own mother who had suddenly burst. Aubrey turned to the girl who was now beside him. He knew, he just knew, he could have helped her, but unfortunately for her, he needed her seat at the counter. So she would have to go.

"May I speak? May I say something of a personal nature?" he whispered right against her unsensational, unkissed ear, and did not wait for a reply. But he did notice that she had turned the colour of borsht.

"I want you, I want you to lie down on the floor under these seats — no-one will notice — and I shall get on top of you."

She dashed for the door as if she had heard the sirens, and now he sat opposite the impossible, beautiful eyes, set in a moody noshy face. And he could bear the delectable growing pains between his legs.

This meeting would change his life, he knew, as he tried to spear her eyes with his gaze.

She looked at him briefly, but he was not one to be taken in by beautifully obvious pretence.

"Tell me, what is your name?" His hushed tones drew her amber eyes towards his own. And her eyes melted and coagulated as she trembled and took a bite from her sandwich, which now sported the radiant redness from her yearning lips.

"I did ask your name." He yawned slightly, as if bored.

"Why do you want to know?"

"I must know. Do you mind terribly if I sit here, opposite you?"

She shrugged and took another morsel of meat. "Do as you like," she said with apparent indifference.

The flesh was pink, and here indeed were truly exceptional and passionate ears.

How could she not have existed yesterday? Or even this morning?

"My name is Aubrey," he could see that she was preparing to go, and in a moment they would be lost to each other. He nervously snapped his fingers for her bill. And got it.

"Oh — you shouldn't." Her eyelashes fluttered like a berserk safety curtain.

He paid the bill with a confident right hand whilst his other fumbled in his pocket to find the exact amount he had left. His left hand re-entered the world very, very depressed.

"As a barrister I find these sort of places fascinating," he yawned and inhaled a gigantic gust of Mitsouko.

She seemed to grow taller. "Really? My name is Zena Conway."

107

Her voice had suffered a sea-change and she stood before him, her titties almost reaching out to him, yearned to be fondled. They were scouting parties, going on ahead, warning the rest of her about an approaching enemy. In this case her breasts had brains and soon would be sending back messages to lower the drawbridge.

And her eyes, her beautiful, trusting, fantastic eyes, seemed to drink him all up. "Are you really a barrister?"

"Yes! For my sins." Then he stopped looking at her eyes and concentrated on the rest of her.

* * *

"Isn't it a luxury? Walking!" Zena gaily remarked as they approached Liverpool Street Station. The overcast day had lifted, and the moody English sky blazed with golden light.

"It won't last," he said.

"Oh, you're a pessimist."

"Who in his right mind is anything else?" he replied without looking towards her, not for any special effect but because he had the strong but absurd feeling that she would suck him right into herself and devour him. And he would have been disappointed to be proved wrong.

"I'm glad you're a pessimist," she said. "It's more mature, somehow."

He walked upon the new surface of the world where every grey alleyway suddenly seemed that it would lead to an orchard with no angels guarding the turnstiles with flaming swords.

"Live around here?" He threw the words with a casual disdain that would have made even Belgrave Square sound like a non-salubrious address.

She sighed deeply. It was not a Jewish sigh, just a sigh. But she did not reply to his question.

Outside the police station in Bishopsgate, he stopped walking, closed his eyes, and there she was, obligingly naked and revealing her pink yearning flesh that was without one solitary blemish from top of forehead to tip of big toe.

They continued walking slowly and silently for a while, then he repeated his question. "Zena! Tell me, do you live round here?"

"I'd love to live here, it's so romantic and mysterious." She sighed huskily. "I live between two worlds. Stamford Hill. Most people passed through. We stayed."

"Zena," he gazed at her gravely, "never be ashamed of your origins and where you live. Accept what you are and who you are. It's not your fault if you were not born in the lap of extreme luxury."

Then he saw a cab far down the road, on the other side, so he hailed it.

Both the gloom and the watery grave had receded. And he felt gay as he raised his umbrella high and shouted, "Cab! Cab!", even though the driver had already seen them,

"Cab!"

He was pleased to have remembered that people with position and taste never shouted "Taxi." Small things mattered. He could see how impressed she was and he felt very tall beside her.

"You do not seem to lack confidence," she said rather sadly, obviously comparing him with herself.

"Me? Lack confidence? Good lord, no! Why do you say that?"

"Ah no reason. It's just that everyone seems to lack confidence these days." Then she perked up, smiled and looked up at him with admiration.

The taxi had done a U-turn and was now before them.

"May I drop you somewhere?" he asked.

"Well actually I'm going to Bond Street to have my hair done," she replied.

"Fine!" He turned to the cabbie, "Bond Street, please."

Zena nodded her beautiful head.

"It's good to get away from the hustle and bustle of the Inner Temple. Sometimes I come down here to improve my knowledge of mankind. We have so much to learn from one another." He knew exactly how to talk to her. And with that right amount of indifference and interest to make a woman frankly crazy for him.

Aubrey nestled back into the upholstery. Taxis were so womb-like, so reassuring. "Zena, I have something important to say to you."

She smiled, but did not speak. Her pretty little erotic ears were waiting on his words. "I have taken quite a liking to you. You interest and excite me, Zena."

Remembering the early chapters of the Kama-Sutra, he had an overwhelming desire to kiss the lobes of those ears, but he suppressed it.

109

He would have to be patient and emulate those great heroes of history that he so admired. He would have to wait for at least another day or so before he crossed the Styx, by that far less used route, the return journey from death, to where Zena was waiting to be pumped into passion, and thus back into life.

He patted the soft hand that had never done a stroke of manual labour in all its days or nights.

"How warm you are!" Then he realised the hand was his own, but a modicum of nervousness was only to be expected under the circumstances. Then he patted her hand. "How warm you are," he repeated.

"Only now. I'm usually freezing, but somehow not at this moment. You know what they say, 'cold hands warm heart'." She giggled. It was the first time she had stepped out of character, but he did not wince. Cliché did not destroy her classic sensuality. He just had to have her, proverbs and all. He could easily discard the proverbs later.

"I never feel the cold, I'm always warm like toast." Aubrey opened the window and noticed that it had started raining. A few drops fell into the cab and splashed her face. He leaned over and closed her window.

He dared not think of the things that he dared not think about. So he quickly changed the subject. "I would like to ask you a very direct question and you needn't answer if you do not wish."

"Ask me," she said. He knew she was longing for him to touch her, but he desisted. He simply had to be different in her eyes in order to achieve the same hillocks that all the other swine tried so hard to climb. But he would succeed where they had failed. By slow and brilliant strokes, he would get to the top of her and surmount her, and then slide down into the warm valley beneath, where all her treasure was waiting just for him, in that pulsing, untrodden cave. In other words, within a few days he would push his angry Goliath right up her crack.

What had he to lose? Until Zena his life had been worth nothing. And what had she to gain? Only the thing she desired most to lose, unless he was mistaken. There was no point in beating about the bush.

He leaned towards her, but did not attempt to kiss her. "Zena, are you a virgin?" He used a compound of compassion and gravity in his question. Compassion in case she had been

110

inadvertently raped in Golders Hill Park when she was seventeen, and gravity to show that the condition of her maidenhead, or lack of it, was of some concern to him.

She did not look shocked but replied slowly. "That depends. I'm not really sure, sometimes I believe I am. Why?"

"That's good. That's very good. I'm very pleased with you, Zena. You have the thing I desire most: honesty."

"I've never met a barrister in the flesh before," she said, and her words caused his temples to pound.

"The Law of God is sacred to me, that's why I took the Silk in the first place. And incidentally, you are sacred to me. You are beautiful but sacred. A person of my experience and sensitivity can only afford to indulge in sexual passions within the security and sanctuary of marriage. Apart from the morality, there is also the needless dissipation of vital energy."

"Oh Aubrey, it's so nice to meet a man who can control himself."

"I can for the moment, Zena."

She opened her sweet-smelling African crocodile handbag and handed him a card. "My father is a kosher butcher. Here is our address." Aubrey did not reply because they were approaching Ludgate Circus. Somehow he would have to slip out, and unfortunately leave Zena to pay the fare. But for the moment he was happy, for he still had her for the length of Fleet Street. How marvellous it would have been for both of them if he really could have had her, on the floor of the cab, suddenly, and be discovered by a herd of hungry reporters.

He could just see the stark headlines.

"Aubrey, you ought to join the S.O.S."

"S.O.S.? Who's drowning?" he flipped back.

"It's a charity organisation. We're a group of exgrads. A nice crowd, Jewish of course. S.O.S., stands for the SLIGHTLY OLDER SET. I was against the title. I wanted the MMM — the More Mature Motley. You see we're more mature than other groups. No fashionable pop ideas for us. We indulge in exciting intellectual and cultural activities, besides collecting a fantastic amount for charities, I wish you'd join."

"Aren't you a little young for the SLIGHTLY OLDER SET?"

"Oh, I'm the baby. They spoil me and I love it. You mean to say you've never heard of us? Obviously you haven't been reading the *Jewish Chronicle* recently."

111

"I can see that any organisation needs a mascot, but I would have thought my age might have jeopardised my chances," he remarked casually.

"After all, I'm hardly — slightly older, am I?"

"I would say you might just about qualify, Aubrey. You're borderline — but —"

Then he saw the Law Courts in The Strand. "I'm terribly sorry. The Law Courts! A waiting client."

He looked at his wristwatch, "*Omni pasquia miamonides fugit*," he boomed as he opened the door. "I must dash. Forgive me." But the car still sped along so he tapped on the glass with a threepenny bit, and when the cab stopped he jumped out. "Forgive me?"

"Of course. Never keep a customer waiting. Please phone me." She leaned forward to show she meant it. "Please!"

"Fear not. I shall tinkle you sooner than you imagine."

"Aubrey, are you married?"

He shook his head slowly.

"Why not?" she said with incredulity. "Everyone who hasn't got problems should be married."

"Law has been my obsession, my sweet girl, and I must be sure. I could not give myself to anyone. I have my honour and my pride to consider. I have also been exceedingly busy. It is only recently that I have considered sharing my life with someone else. My flourishing practice practically runs itself now, so all in all one could say I am ready."

Her hot mouth suddenly kissed him, "I like you, Aubrey," she purred huskily. "Please phone me."

"Oh dear, I really must dash — and I don't seem —" he was going through pockets as he was tearing himself away.

"Don't worry. I'll pay. I'm going furthest."

He smiled benignly.

"And if you lose my card I'm in the book, under my father's name: Lewis Conway 'Kosher Butcher'. And please join."

"I'd love to join you, in any exciting venture. Groups normally bore me, but for you — I'd love to join."

"Groups bore me too, but you know what mothers are. They think twenty-five is two thousand years too late." Her safety curtains went up and down several times. Then they stayed up. And she sighed plaintively. He wasn't sure, but it could almost have been a Jewish sigh, in embryo.

He closed the door, smiled through the glass and mouthed benignly, "Trust me,"

Then he turned to the cabbie, "Speed on."

The taxi whizzed away, and Aubrey held his hand high, in Maccabean salutation.

He had done right not to seem too eager. Jewish girls, like time bombs, had to be opened very, very slowly and with fanatical care, if one was not to be deprived of a lifetime of blissful liberties. He went over to a newspaper vendor.

"*Evening Standard* please." He offered four coins, "Keep the penny change."

"Yes, sir. Thanks, sir. And that'll be another penny. You're living in the past, sir."

Aubrey parted with his last coin, then he looked around to see which side of the road he was on.

As soon as he got his bearings, he strolled slowly in the direction of his home.

———————————

from **Settle Down Simon Katz**

Simon slowed his pace as soon as he left the main road, and when he turned into Wentworth Street he stood still, and breathed it in.

The main road had become a nightmare; the *kishkers* had been pulled out of it, and the old decrepit structures lay buried beneath the new, tall, clean supershell. Everything now was clean and dead, dead with a monotony of faces, faces with dead eyes trapped behind glass and steel, faces hurtling between nowhere and nowhere.

But the market place had not changed all that much since he was a boy. At least this oasis was still there. And even if the limbs of the community had withered away, the spine was still intact and the body was still breathing. Just about. Still, one had to be thankful for small mercies.

And as he drank in the sight of the small bustling crowd around him, he felt a sense of relief.

Around the corner was home. And Betty. But he would rest awhile here, for here were the smells: the timeless smells of oranges and rotten cabbages. No doubt one day they would get rid of all the smells, and people would be born without noses. Meanwhile, one had to relish such things while they lasted.

He always dawdled along Wentworth Street like this on his way home, because there was always time to pass.

It was not a new realisation either, this awareness that there was a dwindling of shapes he knew, this disappearance of faces he recognised. For they were all gone. It was as if they had been called out of the sunlight, one by one, but gradually; gradually so that you didn't notice. But now there definitely was a dearth of people; they had been yanked out of the market place of life, and pulled into dark doorways and thrown down into rotting cellars.

Almost everyone he knew was now busy occupied elsewhere, decomposing in the darkness. Betty was a decomposer, and his father, and his mother. And his brother. And his sister. They were all decomposers. But not him, not yet.

From *Settle Down Simon Katz*, a novel (1973)

114

There were always these sudden moments like this, when you realised that the gradual evacuation had taken all the faces out, the way a bomb takes out a city. And you felt isolated and alone, and, whistling, you pretended to be interested in the price of oranges, and you handled the cucumbers.

Gone were the cucumber salesmen he used to know, and the pickled-herring sellers. And the beigel seller. The faces he once nodded to. The faces who nodded back to him.

There were still plenty of people about, but they were not the same. New tongues haggled. New faces stared. Brown fingers poked the yams and the mangoes. Things change. One just had to accept. His people were all gone.

A few stragglers remained, for their own reasons. They stayed behind, scratching and scrabbling around the huddle of streets. But the main tribe had moved on; moved far away from these timeless smells of distemper and carbolic.

The Jews had moved away forever. But the ghosts were still clinging to the roofs of tenements; tenements that were no longer there. Faces stared, pressed against panes of glass from windows shattered and pulverised to dust ages ago. Faces from the past, smiling, crying, calling. All without sounds. Faces merging together; faces flying out of time from between the never-ending wars of bombs, poverty and affluence. Gone faces. Faces belonging to people who were gone into the ground, or into Golders Green, Finchley, or Wembley Park, or Jerusalem.

Simon laughed out loud, but it didn't matter. In the East End, people were used to people. And people were very strange creatures. No one would take any notice. He would sooner settle in Jerusalem than Wembley Park, and he would never go to Jerusalem.

Alan, his terrible son, lived at Wembley Park, with his terrible wife. And they kept him away from his beautiful grand-daughter. There they were committing a monstrous crime, and they were getting away with it. Imagine bringing up a beautiful gifted child in Wembley Park! How could they do that to him? And to her? And to themselves?

He knew he would never leave here, even though he had never allowed himself to mix with people who lived around here. He knew nobody. And nobody knew him. But then, who knew anyone? He and Betty had never indulged in the community. He and his next door neighbours had always been total strangers. 'Thank God.'

When Betty had been alive they had enjoyed each other's company from the very day they met. They had kept themselves to themselves and had not needed anyone. She had been his wife, lover, adviser, companion and neighbour, all rolled into one. And now she was gone, he had withdrawn even further away from those who surrounded him.

He stopped at the fruit stall. There was a beautiful pyramid of William pears. The price tag had a motto. 'Don't squeeze me until I'm yours.' Who took notice of such things in the East End? He picked one up, and held it, like he was valuing an ornament. "A lovely juicy William pear, you can't beat it."

The greengrocer nodded, took the pear, weighed it, and was about to put it in a bag. Simon quickly restrained him: "No, no, no. Too much wrapping goes on in the world. Anyway, it's got its own wrapping. How much?" He paid, sank his teeth into it, and closed his eyes to savour the flesh. There was something eternal about a pear. You could rely on pears. He felt very pleased with himself as he walked away.

"I say?" The greengrocer was calling him back. "Can I have a word with you?"

So he complied, and he wiped the dripping juice away from his chin. He even smiled. Politeness was a commodity that was in short supply. The world could do with a lot more. "Yes? Can I help you?"

The man replied with a persecuted wail. It sounded altogether too emotional for what he was saying. "For years I've seen you pass by. Sometimes you buy a pear, sometimes an orange. Sometimes nothing. For years and years, and I don't even know your name. I don't know what you do."

"Listen, all I want is a pear, not a relationship."

"Look! Don't get me wrong, I'm not nosey. But I take an interest in my customers."

"That's nice. Goodbye."

But the man was holding on to his shoulder; he was a *meshuggener*. "Do you know, you are a lucky man."

"What do you mean?" Simon always tried to be civil, unless it was utterly impossible. So far, the man hadn't really offended.

"What I mean is, I see you walking around, it's obvious you're a retired gentleman. That's why you're lucky. I can't wait to retire. It must be marvellous to do nothing all day, to have a rest."

"I'll rest in my grave." He was a bloody fool. Like so many people, he couldn't wait to be thrown on the scrap heap.

"What do you do then if you're not retired? How do you pass the time?"

"I mind my own business."

The man smiled weakly, and Simon walked away. He was about to go straight home, but the man with the bloody fingers, quartering boiling fowls at the poultry stall, jogged his memory. It was Friday afternoon and the Sabbath lay stretched before him. The queen. The bride. The beautiful Sabbath. That time in space that made you believe that you could step back from the rat-race and separate yesterday from tomorrow. The Sabbath was a dam holding off the engulfing waters of forever; it protected you from next week.

Simon was sure that it wasn't his imagination. He could already smell the first tangible threads of the Sabbath. He raised his nose to the sky, and sniffed in the holy smell, the collective libation, the magic liquid: the chicken soup. The bubbling saucepans were now being stirred in preparation for the Sabbath, and the smell was rising from the kitchens of those few of the tribe who still remained. The aroma was unmistakable as it hovered above him. A golden cloud in the prematurely darkening sky.

———

Exile

It is raining outside.
It is raining.
The wet leaves are rotting into the earth,
into the sockets of my father's song,
into the mouth of my mother's skull
where she smiles for all eternity.

I am clutched by a cold sadness,
by loneliness, by loss.
Where do I belong?
I feel far away.
But far away from where?

It is raining outside;
far away from the wind on the hills of my dream,
from the pipes and the birds of my song.

My son laughs in a strange language,
a language I understand too well.

Perhaps I should take my life and death with me,
walk with my wife and my son and two blankets,
into the rain.

From *Erica, I Want to Read You Something* (1967)

from The Dissent of Dominick Shapiro

He stood against the wall, a few doors away from The Sheraton, watching his relatives crowding into the revolving doors. None recognised him as he slouched against the highly polished exterior in Bond Street. The Shapiros, the Lazaruses, the Marcuses and the Conways all came under his scrutiny and ridicule. Not one single member of the family would escape his contempt. They had nothing he wanted, these relatives of his. Those neanderthal nephews and neolithic nieces, those uncouth uncles and crappy cousins.

No one noticed him except the doorkeeper of the hotel who probably thought he was trying to steal something.

He had not gone to the synagogue. They had begged him but even they could see that he would not be moved by their hysterical argument. They finally gave in when he struck a bargain.

"I will not trouble you on Monday morning. I will go to school as quiet as a Trappist Monk if you let me off the synagogue."

There was never any question that he would not come to this reception. He wouldn't miss this for the world.

So he had come straight to Bond Street. His mother and father and Alex and Sharon and Malcolm and baby Dawn had not yet arrived. Neither had the bride and groom. They were at this moment being immortalised by 'Boris! Society Photographer of Class and Distinction.'

So cousin Fiona and her fat Antony were now as one. Served them right. And what was all that crap about all brides being beautiful? It just went to show what a load of old cobblers proverbs were. But if not beautiful she was not uncomely.

Now most of the tribe were inside and his father's car swept around the corner. He pressed himself further into a doorway as they all emerged, laughing. But there was no putting it off. He would have to enter now under the eye of that female eagle, his mother; otherwise he would probably get punched in the face by that stormtrooper who guarded the door. And he would end up for the rest of the evening spilling his blood into the sickening Sunday loneliness of Bond Street.

From *The Dissent of Dominick Shapiro*, a novel (1966)

"Lo!" he shouted at them, just as they were about to go inside. And as predicted 'the uniform' came forward with moronic face clenched for violence.

"Dominick!" she called as she saw him. She pulled him to her. "It's all right, my good man. This is my son." Stormtrooper retreated.

They all stood around him, gasping.

"How could you Dominick! How could you!"

She was probably referring to the fact that he was wearing his fur coat and hat. Lew cupped his hands over his eyes, then looked again.

"He's off his rocker!" Alex said.

"And you bought him a new suit," Malcolm said.

"Mummy! We'll be a laughing stock," Sharon said. But they all continued smiling because of the other guests still entering The Sheraton. It was very hard for them.

"What have you got on underneath?" Paula unbuttoned the coat and squirmed at his favourite navy roll neck sweater. "And jeans!" She buttoned up the coat again.

"Go home at once and get changed," Lew shouted.

"This coat was good enough for my great-grandfather. It's good enough for me and that lot, in there. Besides, I'm bringing tradition back into the old corpse called a family."

"Wait until I get you home."

Just then Uncle Nat approached. He was a distant first cousin of his father. Distant because he was not quite entirely in the world; just that little bit slow on the uptake. But he had his head screwed on as far as money was concerned. Uncle Nat laughed when he saw his nephew.

"I offer you my condolences Lew. Take no notice. He wants to attract attention." Nat placed his arm around Lew's neck and pulled him towards the revolving door. Lew shrugged, helpless. "It's all part of the teenage myth," Uncle Nat was explaining as he waved the family towards the interior.

God. So now he fancied himself as a philosopher. The daydreams of pygmies were more frightening than the nightmares of giants.

"That's right," Lew said, entering. "Why should I worry? Everyone knows I tried my best."

"Put at least a buttonhole in that terrible coat," Paula said, pinning a white carnation to the fur.

Inside, the Jewish Major Domo announced them. "Mr and Mrs Lew Shapiro and family." He boomed across the hall. Major Domo's eyes nearly leapt from their sockets when he saw Dominick. He quickly looked away, refused to believe and went on booming.

"He's in fancy dress," Lew laughed loudly, trying to explain away the apparition. But no one seemed to be the slightest bit interested; they were all busy at the buffet eating and drinking. Filling in the time until the bride and groom arrived, when they could get down to the main business of eating and drinking.

Dominick made a bee-line for the drinks bar where he climbed on to a high stool in the corner. "Whiskey please. Double!" He would get wonderfully sloshed tonight.

The bartender looked dubious, but Fiona's father's brother's brother-in-law, who was supervising the drinks and was also there to make sure that none of the waiters or bartenders pinched a bottle, nodded. He got his whiskey. And he drank it down in one hot gulp.

"Another double whiskey please." And Fiona's father's brother's brother-in-law nodded again, gravely. It was like fire entering his veins, transmuting him into a golden bird of incredible beauty. And another and another. And his fingertips were singing. He was careful to keep his hands tight between his knees, otherwise he would soar above them and zoom between the chandeliers.

And after all, why should he claim attention? It wasn't his night. Under the tents of Mayfair the children of Israel were assembled for the marriage of Fiona and Antony. Good job they didn't have to cross the Red Sea tonight. He and his reflection laughed together when he visualised Paula with a bundle of *matzos* on her back, trekking the deserts of North Finchley.

The hall was spinning quite nicely now. He was well and truly sloshed and he felt marvellous.

"Double whiskey encore!" His voice sounded resolute but he knew he was balancing on the edge of the abyss.

"No more liquid gold in the veins," he said to Fiona's father's brother's brother-in-law. And Fiona's father's brother's brother-in-law nodded.

They were not all terrible. Three or four at least out of the assembled three hundred were bearable. His mother floated across and kissed him on the cheek and straightened the flower on his great-grandfather's coat. "Be a good darling. Don't drink too much."

"Mother. I — rather like you. You mean well."

"I know darling, you mean to be a good boy."

"For Gawd's sake leave me alone."

She floated off again. There would be no cataclysm tonight. And it was just as well, for who could survive the earthquake and flood? Who of these soft pink relatives could cross the desert?

A girl's face loomed close. He recognised it from somewhere. She was only a child last year but now she had breasts, and desire in her eyes for him. She was a second cousin from some side of the family. Her name eluded him. She could not fly, she was useless.

The bar soared away. It was just as well. He stood under ferns just smiling at everyone.

"Hello! How are you? I'm fine! How's your wife? Good!" "How are your kids? Doing well? Lovely! That's the stuff." Who were they? Who on earth were these relatives of his?

But he could not float away altogether, he could not lie on the floor. He would not be explained away as a mere drunken eccentric. He would show them all how a true Shapiro carried himself.

Many people were looking at the seating plan; to see who they were sitting next to at dinner.

"I'm not sitting next to him."

"I won't sit with her."

"If I don't sit at that table I'm leaving." He had been to several weddings in his sixteen years and this same scene had taken place at all of them. Some were surreptitiously swapping cards around; others were seeking the bride's mother, to make a strong protest.

But mostly the guests seemed content; even a batch of usually melancholic aunts were smiling. The Shapiros, the Lazaruses, the Marcuses and the Conways were making an attempt at peaceful coexistence.

He could tales unfold. Tales that the *News of the World* would not be ashamed to print. Tales of the family. Luscious tales of unlawful sex. Beautiful tales of uncles and nieces, of aunts and cousins, coveting and possessing flesh that was not their own freehold. Tales that he had heard whilst pretending to be asleep on divans and armchairs. Tales whispered and hissed between

Lew and Paula, tales designed to anger the other during bitter arguments.

"My Lords, Ladies and Gentlemen, your bride and groom," Domo boomed. All went quiet and the band played Here Comes The Bride. Everyone froze at the buffet as Fiona and Antony entered the hall.

Then the throng burst forward to kiss and congratulate, and hand the envelopes containing the cash and the cheques to the bridegroom, who looked like a window model for the outsize department of Selfridges.

"Wish you joy."

"Please God by you!"

"Please God by your grandchildren."

Everyone was shaking hands and congratulating and kissing everyone.

Fiona as a matter of fact looked pretty hot stuff. He wouldn't have minded being Antony, just for tonight. He had never fancied her before now, but now he could see that she probably would be able to perform quite nicely for a few months. She smiled across at him, and winced charmingly at his beautiful clobber.

He would never play the leading male role in this wedding scene. He would never stand in a hall like this, dressed like that, furiously slipping envelopes of money into his inner pocket. He would never get married. Fionas only stayed hot for a limited season.

He looked at the plan to see where he was sitting. Blast them to Hades. They had put him on the children's table. He was seated between over-ripe Renata and adenoidal Maurice. Both first cousins, their faces were covered with horrible spots, both fifteen years old. An obnoxious age to be.

He would demand to be seated with the adults. Not that they were any more enlightened. It was merely the principle of the thing. No, he would protest and walk out. No! He would walk out without protesting.

What the hell! He would neither protest nor walk out. They were all beneath his contempt. If a God walked amongst mortals he could afford to be magnanimous.

Dinner was nigh. You could feel it. Meat was in the offing, the atmosphere was changed by tribal electricity charged by hunger.

The band was automatically churning through *mazurkas* and

horas. The players wore smiles but their eyes were so terribly bored as they roamed around the congregation. This was the scene of every Sunday; so memorable to each bride and groom, so incredibly similar to the players.

One plonked the bass and another plucked the guitar, one brushed the drums and the mustachioed Don Juan of a bandleader scraped the strings of his shmaltzy violin.

He saw his parents sitting together on a silver wickerwork settee. He sidled close and hid himself behind the inevitable ferns.

"To be a parent is impossible," Lew said.

"It's ridiculous. It's terrifying," Paula said.

"If they succeed it hurts because they leave you anyway," Lew said. "They just go off and get married." God, he was in a black mood.

"And if they fail it hurts. It all hurts," Paula sighed. But then she soon smiled. "Doesn't Fiona look out of this world. Mind you, she's not a patch on Sharon. Sharon was the prettiest bride ever. Everyone said so."

"Yes," Lew replied. Dominick fled the little scene and returned to the bar. But it had just closed.

"We're closed because dinner is ready," said Fiona's father's brother's brother-in-law. "Besides, you've had more than enough."

Then it occurred to him. He was not exactly a God tonight. He was more like an avenging angel. Scores had to be settled. A wonderful feeling of power started surging right through him and he didn't quite know how he could contain his excitement.

But of one thing he was sure, he had to be patient if he was to strike. This thing had to be done with superb style.

"My Lords! Ladies! And Gentlemen! Pray take your places for dinner!"

He rushed with the rest of them to his appointed place, and his feet stamped to the gay crappy music as he dug straight into his pineapple boat.

"Lo Dominick! 'member me?" Renata, fluttering her eyelashes, leaned close. No doubt she thought she was being sexy.

He growled back. "Yer!" And he turned away.

Yes, he would bide his time. First he would enjoy the meal.

Smoked salmon! Ugh! A whole plate of it. Disgusting. What

did he care for food? When he departed forever from the North West Frontier he would live only on sausages and chips and baked beans. He squeezed the lemon on to the smoked salmon. And ate it in one go.

Then chicken soup. "Aaaaah!" He growled.

All the kids at the table looked up, terrified.

Everybody was eating too much. It was perfectly nauseating to watch them ladling the liquid down their gullets. What did they care about the starving masses of India and Pakistan? The soup tasted good. Surprisingly good. He asked the waitress for more, but the bloody old owl of a cow only wanted to shove plates on the table and pull them off again at breakneck speed. Waitresses hated serving at the children's table; there wasn't much gratitude shown by way of money.

Then came the ox tongue and stuffed neck of chicken and *blintzes* and grilled tomatoes and mushrooms.

"Please, before you go, another slice of that delicious tongue."

The waitress grudgingly complied. It was disgusting; this meat-eating. One day he would become vegetarian, wear rope sole sandals and cotton clothing. Meanwhile he would have to remain a hypocrite and eat the scrumptious chunks of meat. He couldn't afford to have a full conscience yet. There would be plenty of time after his seventeenth birthday.

Then, in the middle of all that delectable food, came ice cream sherbet. Surely it was a mistake. They hadn't had the main meat course yet.

"Why have you given me dessert?"

"You should know there always is ice cream sherbet, halfway." The pretentious bitch. He did remember now, casting his mind backwards in time to the last wedding. Maybe it was just as well, for all the others seemed beaten already. As for him, it had been up until now, quite a passable hors d'oeuvres.

The band were playing the inevitable *Hava Nagila* and the Master of Ceremonies stood up in his hunting scarlet and held up his hands to shush everyone.

"LADIES — AND — GENTLEMEN — YOUR BRIDEGROOM WILL NOW DRINK — WITH ALL THE GOOD LOOKING YOUNG LADIES."

There was a gale of laughter as all the aunts and nieces and cousins and sisters and daughters and grannies and wives, from six to seventy, stood up, and waved their glasses at Fat Antony.

The band went into its automatic tune for this occasion. "Put me amongst the girls."

And the same thing happened with the bride and all the men. Fabulous Fiona, luscious and ripe, held out her glass while the band chugged, "All the nice girls love a sailor."

And all the men and boys stood swaying and waving their glasses. Dominick shuddered when he thought of Fat Antony on top of her. The waiters came marching in with huge steaming platters, and soon, his arms surrounding his plate and his head tucked well down, he descended upon the mountain of food. The roast capon, the French potatoes and brussels sprouts.

Then his one arm sufficed to hold the fort as his eyes darting round the table directed his other hand to the Chianti, the Palestinian wine and the Spanish olives, the pickled herring and Dutch cucumbers. All these he pulled close to him, away from the reach of Moronic Maurice and all the dribbling four year olds. Then he mixed the two wines together into his long glass and topped it all with the champagne that he grabbed from a passing waiter.

"Hey! That's not yours. No champagne on the kids' table."

He snarled back at the waiter who decided that discretion was the better part of valour. This would probably be the last proper meal he would have for years and years.

Then appeared the fruits and liqueurs and coffee and cakes and chocolates and petits fours and almonds and sweets and nuts. Such stinking affluence. He lined his pockets with doylies and scooped up the sweetmeats and dropped them in. Two of the children cried, but he could not afford to be too kind. He gave them a sweet each. All this would have to serve him in the desert.

He waved across to his mother who blew him a kiss. He was feeling quite hot in the coat so he took it off. Renata moved away and wiggled in her chair. She had obviously got a whiff of him and he was amazed she didn't like it. What on earth was wrong with after shave lotion? They were never satisfied, these people. His mother had nagged him to have a bath that morning, so he did. And he poured the whole bottle over his body after she called through the door, "Come out smelling sweet, please dolly."

It just proved that you should never compromise. He thought he smelled just fine.

Someone started praying. An old man with watering eyes

looking quite demented, *davened* backwards and forwards, making droning foreign sounds. It was Hebrew. It didn't mean a thing to him. He was sorry now he hadn't learned it. It was all their fault; they just gave in to him, they never made him do a thing he didn't want. How could you respect someone who insisted on giving you your own way? Well, about most things. They were just flabby. He smiled now at his father.

He didn't mind the praying man. At least he was sincere, at least he believed in what he was doing. There were far worse things than grace after meals. Grace before meals, for instance. But not apparently for these people, who were shuffling their feet and coughing and chatting and pulling faces. They had no dignity, no discipline.

He liked the old man. He dug the old man. That old man was way out.

He looked for the way out and noted it. One had to be prepared for any contingency. He felt cold again so he put on his coat. Everybody else was sweating. He was sure his great-grandfather was not like this lot. They had no prayers; they were people without. The without people.

In this coat you could cross the desert. In this coat you could defy the Arctic wastes.

A great yawn was going on. All the little yawns were becoming one huge gawping gap. And such a stretching of arms.

And even he had to agree that enough was enough. If that old man didn't stop moaning he would personally go over and ram his prayer book down his throat. This was no idle threat. He would do it. Now!

But that old man with watering eyes had fantastic survival capacity, for at that precise moment he snapped the book closed, wiped his eyes and uttered "Amen."

"Amen! Amen!" came out like a great sigh of relief. Grace after meals had taken thirty-five minutes.

He would have shown them. And he would still show them, for the best was yet to come. Baby Dawn looked across, apprehensively. He did not disappoint her; he crossed his eyes.

The drama was moving to a swift climax because the speeches were about to begin. The Major Domo was banging the table with his little wooden hammer. "MY LORDS — LADIES — AND GENTLEMEN — Pray silence for —" he looked at a slip of paper "for Uncle Reuben."

127

"I have known the bridegroom for many years!" Applause. Uncle Reuben silenced them. Uncle Reuben was a dab hand at controlling crowds. "But, I have known the bride even longer."

More applause. Uncle Reuben with his ginger hair, gave a sly wink. Everyone appreciated the subtle undertones. "No! No! It's only my jokes. She's not only a good girl, Fiona is the goodest girl there ever was. Need I tell you? Doesn't everybody know and love this — flower."

The actors of the drama were all assembled. Aunts and uncles were smiling across tables. Cousins were cuddling. Everyone was melted into smiles. Here they all were.

The skeletons were no longer in the cupboards, they were dancing in the living room. The whispers of years were about to be shouted aloud. But not by Uncle Reuben, who was still waxing poetical.

"For to me she is likened to a flower. Fiona! What a beautiful sound! What a beautiful name! Fiona! It rolls off the tongue. The letters themselves spell out her beauty. F for..."

Dominick was sorely tempted and had to shove his fist into his mouth.

"...for fragrance. I for intelligence..." Why was it on occasions like this everyone started spouting poetically? Tonight scrap dealers and bookmakers would become Laureates.

"And her father. Barry. What can I say of her father?" Everyone clapped. Uncle Reuben seemed lost for words for a moment as he stood convexly important, his hands holding his lapels. Everyone knew what he could really say about his brother Barry.

"What can I say about my dear brother Barry? The man who, with his dear wife Zelda, brought up this flower from a bud to a bloom. What can I say of him?"

They were waiting.

"As everyone knows, Barry is a man of high principle. He is a printer. A printer of renown and high quality. He is a man of his word."

The applause gave him a new incentive and his eyes burned with intensity and his hands were outstretched, as he soared higher and higher, intoxicated on his own words.

"His life indeed closely resembles his profession; it can be likened unto a printing press. The great plateau of his years, set out on the machine of the world; set out truthfully, clearly, indelibly, by God, the great editor, to print a clear impression upon the scroll of life."

This was marvellous stuff. Dominick clapped wildly.

But Uncle Reuben wasn't finished yet. "The printed word, my friends, as everyone knows, is, the manifestation, of truth, and fidelity, and dignity. And that has been his life. May his children, especially Fiona, follow his example which should be a beacon to all of us."

He wouldn't sit down and he quelled their applause. "Listen. One final word. Bear with me. Let us remember and copy his example. The way he has worshipped his own darling wife, Zelda, and cherished her with the words and the ink and the pressure of his toil."

No one could have suppressed this storm of applause. Uncle Reuben sat down and Uncle Barry kissed Zelda and pulled Fiona close and squeezed her.

This was it. As much as he admired his Uncle Barry he would have to suffer. Because he was a dirty old beautiful villain and his background story was the juiciest. He jumped up onto the table and he didn't have to call for attention. A sea of frozen staring faces looked up at him.

"Now let's examine Uncle Barry a bit closer."

His mother, dreamlike amongst all that stillness, rushed over and tugged at his coat. "Dominick! Shut up!" No one would stop him.

The band started playing. "Dear old pals — jolly old pals." But the music petered down to a saxophone and then faded completely; this was probably due to the fact that the bandleader was more interested in what Dominick had to say than in moving his fingers up and down, up and down.

There was a suicidal silence. As if they wanted him up there spilling the beans. No one really tried to get him down. Even his mother was just staring up at him.

"There's not another family as united as ours." A faint voice from a great aunt wailed.

"Now everyone knows that Uncle Barry is having Cousin Rosalind. He's been having her for years. His own niece."

And the walls came tumbling down.

The main table was overturned and the bride rushed out screaming with Fat Antony in hot pursuit.

"I avenge! I avenge! I denounce this travesty of a family."

129

His father was trying to pull him down and he felt strangely calm and blissful. Through all the chaos he noticed a waiter shoving a chicken under his apron, whilst another emptied a box of cigars.

"This is the end," his mother wailed.

"Wait till I get you home." His father's fist pressed against his nose. And now he was on the floor and his mother's arms were flung wide, trying to hold back the horde who were trying to get at him, "Leave him alone, he's only a child."

And Alex came forward and he was smiling. Surely he wasn't going to congratulate him? That wasn't like Alex.

WHAM! SMACK!

All the stars burst through the roof and shattered the chandeliers. Someone had sloshed him good and hard; full in the face. It didn't hurt him one bit.

He was floating, floating right out of the scene; he was floating over the disturbed ant-heap. The band played furiously as if they were clockwork that had been overwound.

He was being carried out of the hall; away from the hands that were trying to tear him, away from the gargoyle faces that scared him; away from the family face; away from the skeletons dancing amongst the debris.

"We're a happy family! A happy family," an old aunt implored two cousins busy slogging it out. "The happiest family in the world."

And on his way out, apart from all the little fights, he distinctly saw Uncle Barry and Cousin Rosalind's husband, Roland, knocking hell out of each other. And poor Auntie Zelda, looking so alone amongst her weeping sisters. And he had caused all this. But it was perfectly ridiculous. They all knew it anyway. No one ever spoke about it, not openly, but everyone knew,

"I dissent! I dissent! I renounce these festivities!" Alex and Malcolm and his father had carried him out like a dead prince; and now he stood on his own two swaying feet. Aunty Hetty rushed out into the hall and tried to claw him. It pleased him that they hated him so much.

"It's true anyway! He only said the truth," Paula said. Truth did not apparently impress Aunty Hetty. "He should go to prison. He should get locked up."

But the two policemen coming through the revolving doors did impress Aunty Hetty and she retreated back into the chaos of the ballroom. But they were still fighting in the foyer. They were still screaming in the foyer.

What had he done? Had he gone too far or not far enough?

Maybe after all, it was all a dream. That would be too bad. That would be awful. He was bundled out into the street by his immediate relatives, and his last sight of the wedding was the cousins rolling over and punching each other in the thick carpet, and the sound of the band playing happy Hebrew melodies, and aunts wailing "We're a happy family! There's not another family so happy."

The air struck him. It was just as if he had walked into a wall. And another thing struck him. Alex had hit him in the face, inside. Alex had socked him full in the kisser. And Alex had smiled when he did it.

Baby Dawn was cooing somewhere. He felt sorry. Sorry for Aunt Zelda and the old man with watery eyes who prayed. As for the rest of them? He had washed his hands.

So, it was Alex. It had always been Alex. He remembered now what he had forgotten. And for some weird reason, purposely forgotten. Alex was the enemy. It wasn't Baby Dawn and Malcolm at all. They were nothing. They were no threat. It had been Alex. Alex had done this before. Years before. Alex had hit him in the face before. Alex was a swine. Alex would get what was coming to him. Alex was the reason he had to get away.

He smiled at Alex. Alex smiled back. They were in a car or something. Yes. It was a car. The silent backs of parents were just in front of him. So it was Alex. He heard the screeching in the rain. His father was travelling fast.

"Open the window someone." And he was sick and sick and sick. He was vomiting out the family. He had to get away from his brother.

"Hello Malcolm. Baby Dawn, give me a kiss." But she was asleep. This was the turning point. Now he knew. It was Alex who hit him, hard, like Cain. Blood! That was the salt taste in his mouth.

"Blood! Look Mum! Blood!"

It was caked around his lip. His blood. His own precious blood had been spilled. His beautiful blood. It was still trickling.

"Look, I'm still bleeding." His mother turned and stroked his cheek.

"It's only a little cut," she said.

"Little cut." She was an impossible exaggerating woman. "Alex. I hate you. I know you for what you are." He tasted the blood as it trickled into his mouth. It was good.

"Alex, prepare to meet thy doom."

And his smart quiet genius brother, everyone's favourite, behind his intellectual glasses, giving his usual clean smile, hissed, "Shut up, you stupid little swine."

This was it. War had been declared. He had forced the pace. Things had come to a head; things stopped spinning.

He leaned out and the icy air rushed at his face. He had a feeling nothing would be the same again. Then he returned to the quiet of the interior as the Humber roared northwest.

He loved the quiet. For the first time that he could remember, the Shapiros were quiet. Why the hell didn't his father speak. He hadn't said one word. This was ominous.

"Chaos, embrace me. I love you." By the time they reached the house he was sober. Too sober. But he was glad to leave the car because it smelled sour.

They all trooped in.

"Don't hit him Lew," Paula said, standing between father and son. There was altogether too much silence in the house. Sharon took Baby Dawn upstairs, and came down again, and in all that time Lew had still not uttered one word. He just stared at his son. And Sharon and Malcolm were just standing around because they probably thought it would be quite exciting and different for a change. As for Alex, he stood smugly, like a person in the front row at a public execution.

"A thrashing! A real old-fashioned thrashing!" Lew was nodding as if he had finally come up with the solution.

"It was true. Everything Dominick said was true. Thank God we have values and standards." Well anyway, someone was sticking up for him. "Thank God we passed on those values to our kids. It was all true," Paula said.

"So what if it is true? The boy has gone too far this time."

"If you touch me I'll leave home. Forever."

"Right! I'll call your bluff. See how far you'll go."

"Good! Throw me out then! Throw me out!" He could not stifle the sob that got caught up with his words. He felt ashamed of the sob. Alex had noticed the sob. But he was sure that he could hold back the tears. He had to.

"I'm going now. And it's good riddance to all of you and school and every stinking lousy thing in this rotten family." So that was the truth of it. They didn't care if you stayed or went. Parental affection. That was the expression. What a joke!

But his mother held the door closed as he pulled on it.

"Are you out of your mind Lew. He'll leave this house tonight over my dead body."

"If he wants to go let him go. He's a man of the world now." He saw his father wink. As usual Lew was so sure that he was using the right kind of subtle psychology.

"What an obvious little man you are." That was telling him. There was no turning back now. The die was cast.

"Right. Get out of this house before I kick you out. And don't come back until you apologise."

"Never! Never! Never!" He swept out into the garden and strode towards the road, but it was pouring with rain so he sheltered under the tall chestnut. It didn't give much protection but it didn't matter. At last the beautiful moment had arrived. He had attained the loneliness and the aloneness that every individual craved and needed, to be truly born.

She came out after him. He didn't want to hurt her but it was inevitable. Mothers were bound to suffer; mothers like Paula.

"I thought you might be hungry." She offered him an apple. He didn't want to hurt her feelings too much, so he took it.

"Thanks." He knew he was difficult; he wasn't kidding himself on that score; sometimes he thought that children like him shouldn't be inflicted upon parents. But then he saw Alex looking down from his bedroom window. The face of the dark intellectual genius God peeping through his curtain. And then his humility scarpered. In comparison with Alex he was a gift to any parents.

And in the other upstairs window there were Malcolm and Sharon staring down. He could not see his father.

"What have you done you naughty boy? How could you do it?"

"This is the beginning. I was born today."

"It'll all blow over. You terrible boy. What can I do with you?"

But he had to admit that she wasn't going her usual full blast. She had quietened down recently; he had noticed that. Maybe she had emerged through the crunch of her menopause.

"I'll be all right Mother. I'll go to sea."

"What? In winter?" She laughed bitterly.

She could only see the sea in terms of cruises. She was asleep;

that was her trouble. Just another one of the sleepwalking dead. She pushed two five pound notes in his hand. He waved them away. Did she think she could buy him over. She persisted. "Come tomorrow dolly! When Dad isn't here. I'll make peace. Take the money then."

What could you do? She'd only worry her guts out if she thought of him wandering around stony broke. For her sake he took the money.

"Sleep tonight at your friend's house."

"Friend? I have no friend."

"What about David. Go to David."

"David was years ago."

"He was here for your birthday."

"All right. David was months ago."

"Sleep tonight at David's. Good! For my sake. That's settled. Come tomorrow to eat. We'll go to the pictures. If you need anything phone me."

So suddenly she seemed satisfied; she had convinced herself that he was going round to that slob. She had a fantastic technique for not facing the truth.

"You forget I'm leaving home. I dissent Mother. I dissent from everything you stand for." He slipped the two fivers into his fur hat and he was ready for the world.

"Your father is a wonderful man. You don't know what he sacrificed for you," she said.

"I'm a wonderful man. You don't know what I sacrificed for you," Lew shouted from the open kitchen window. She kissed him as he slipped away; he nodded once, threw his head high, and marched through the rain into the shuddery freedom of the night.

* * *

The two of them were quiet in the bedroom for a time. Lew looked across at his wife; she was propped up in bed, pretending to read a book. He wanted her to speak first.

"I was hasty," he said.

She didn't reply.

"I was hasty, wasn't I?"

"Yes," she said.

"He'll come home tomorrow. If not tonight."

134

"If he doesn't it's your fault." She turned over to the wall.

"What he did was a terrible thing. I said, what he did was a terrible thing."

"Huh!"

"He'll be all right. It's me I'm worrying about." Lew sat staring at his face in the mirror.

"What your brother and the rest of them did, and still do, is infinitely worse." He guessed she was right. In a way. But what could you do with such a complicated child? If only he had given Dominick and the others something really tangible to believe in. Could he be blamed if that intangible substance called faith had never descended upon him? How could you pass on something you never had? Yet, why was he torturing himself? What was this thing called faith, suddenly? Why was it nagging at him tonight of all nights? Wasn't a good home and good food and a good education enough? Did he have to feel ashamed for giving his children the real basic essentials? Yet, still there was something lacking. Something wasn't exactly perfect. You couldn't buy faith; that was lacking. If you could buy faith the house of Lew Shapiro would be stacked up to the ceiling with it.

"He's my favourite you know. Dominick. Despite everything."

At last she put down her book. "You shouldn't be so hasty Lew. I'm very annoyed. But I agree, perhaps he did go too far."

So, she was melting; maybe she might even sympathise with him, just for a change.

"That boy. I love him to distraction. What have I done?"

"Don't upset yourself Lew."

"Maybe he'll still be a credit to me." He hated to be pessimistic. Pessimism made him feel so unhappy. He nodded at his reflection.

"Better he should be a credit to himself. Shut up, I'm reading."

Trust her to say the clever thing. She was always so right. She was. Really. That was the trouble. She was hardly ever wrong. And she was so moral. Her morality was crippling. What man in the world could keep up with the morality of Paula Shapiro? She was so right. It was so easy for women to be right. Of course it was better that Dominick should be a credit to himself.

"That's what I meant. To be a credit to me is to be a credit to himself."

"Shush," she said, taking up the book again.

135

And it was quite possible that Dominick might even go the furthest. He didn't know quite in which direction, but there had to be some reason for all that strangeness and complication. "Maybe a genius is not easy in childhood."

"I prefer not to have a genius. I prefer my son." She was right. A fat lot of good genius did to anyone. He couldn't offhand remember seeing one solitary picture of Einstein caught in the act of smiling.

"Maybe he'll be a credit to me, anyway." He still nodded plaintively at the mirror. His reflection understood. Only he understood.

"We owe them everything and they don't owe us a thing. Only their own progress." He listened to his own fine words. The trouble was emotions cut right across fine words and high ideals. They all owed him something no matter how he tried to hold such lofty dreams. Deep down he wanted to be paid back; but what it was exactly they owed him he had never quite fathomed. Recognition maybe? Respect? No! No! They were just empty phrases.

"A child is like a bird. You feed it, you shove food down its throat and the only thanks you get is seeing it fly away," he said. She smiled across at him. Well at least he had her. "I know you're only pretending to read."

She immediately pushed her head close to the book.

He walked to the window and looked out. Maybe his son was hiding behind a tree? Perhaps he should have gone out to look for him?

No, he wasn't there. He felt very uneasy tonight. Out it was all coming, his twice yearly thoughts on life insurance and death and the meaning of life.

The rain unnerved him. Why just tonight did it have to rain so hard? The rain made him feel sad and fearful, but not about Dominick. That boy could take care of himself. A night alone wouldn't do him any harm. It might even bring a fresh understanding to the home. It would all turn out all right in the end. Anyway, with the ten pounds that she had given him he was probably occupying a luxury suite at the Dorchester. He hoped he had gone to that friend of his.

"Maybe we should phone David. Just to make sure he's there."

"Leave him alone, please," he replied. "If we fuss after him it will be worse. He'll hold out longer." Fortunately she was an intelligent woman and could grasp his meaning. But then again he couldn't have married someone who was not above the average.

He went back to the mirror and cried a little, just a little so that she shouldn't notice. And it wasn't tears for his son but tears for himself. For only he knew the truth about his hair; the way he brushed it across to hide his skull. But soon the whole world would know the truth about his loss of hair and power. Lew Shapiro, almost fifty, was winding down, and the hair that remained would be as white as bread; within two years at the most.

His children were pushing him into the earth and his grand-daughter just walked right across him. Only the day before he lay on the settee reading a paper and she just walked across his stomach. (God bless her, as she slept in the next room.)

He had had union with a woman and had been fruitful and he had multiplied. Would all this then turn out to be a minus? If you multiplied did the answer have to be subtraction? Maybe God would yet dawn upon him. Maybe his kids would yet look up to him as he imparted beautiful words of truth and wisdom to them.

Because God had not yet happened there was no reason to believe that he could not arrive suddenly, anytime, and say, "Lew Shapiro, arise. Even if you are bald, I have come to show you the Meaning of Life."

Maybe he would be able to grow old without cursing the loss of hair and happiness and power. Maybe he would be able to slide into the grave without debt or doubt, chortling.

"I'm a failure," he said, as he got into the bed beside her.

She switched off the light. He moved close against her. She moved away. "Get over to your third of the bed," she said. And then she laughed.

"I'm a failure I tell you. A real failure; and I'm afraid."

She turned over towards him and cuddled him and he knew he would be asleep long before her. He couldn't keep his eyes open.

East and West

The copywriter no-world.
The dead jerking incomplete,
the dance of death.
The party goers. The standing lost
with drink in their claws,
in the deserts of their smart flats.
The space sellers.

The armour of expression covering faces
vomiting indifference over the whole
of endless Kensington.

So cancer spreads. People die and burst.
Look! There goes another.
Cancer eats through the walls of their
stomachs, up their lungs,
into their throats,
into their mouths and conversation.

I must get away.
Have I time to fly?
To soar out of these sickening streets?
I must dream that I can escape,
into the arms of my family.
I must embrace the things that made me.

From *Erica, I Want to Read You Something* (1967)

Now they bring their dead to the place of worship.
My family, they sit in rows,
nodding.
It is a building I soon remember.
Incised crumbling walls;
it will stand long after it falls.
So I walk with my praying shadows,
shake their hand.
In the stark stone arena of my play
I see the stoop of my sad father,
and run the other way.

And in that tight room of wailing,
tea handed out with tears and giggles;
pinched cheeks of young girl brides,
speeded up, broken. Buds blown before burst,
blown inward. And here am I, too big for
boots, handed down the evil eye.
Where do I belong?
Here among the washing tubs?

The old men congregate.
The women have a sense of tragic placing
along the Mile End Waste,
crowded with ghosts of playing children.

Tell me I dream as I laugh and sing and scream.

I see the coil of sound leaving my numb mouth,
I snap off the spiral, the plume of sound,
shape it like a paper plane and hurl it into ground
just as my fat sisters take the stairs,
wave their hands so frequently as they climb into clouds.
Their white blobs of pink
flesh blowing in the dark sky.

This is the East, where we lived once.
Where we once loved. Before the West went up,
fell down, pulling the rest.
The West was my growing up. I grew from East to West.
But my feet still cling where I crawled out of the mud bleeding,
and slithered the shores to Aldgate East.

But now the dead are laid down. Look. All my family.
All the members one by one, They carry each other, each in turn.
The living carry the dead away and the dead carry
the living back again.

The old men in my mirror wail.
Their cries split the sky,
cause the thunder to crash and the earth
to heave and the trees to splinter and the
leaves to burn
and the stones to crack and the faces to burst open.

The synagogue explodes.
Then, my grandfathers with the usual blood streaming
from their eyes go down quietly under the great chunks of rock.
And my temple is destroyed. Shot right through.
Night dies. The glass-stained earth.
I am now walking away, somewhat relieved
by the menacing fists of dawn,

At dawn... the world yawns. It's day. Day.
My wife sings. My children, born and unborn play.
At night the worms nibble my dreams away.

from The Hamlet of Stepney Green

*A garden in Stepney Green. A nice day. Sam is lying on a bed.
DAVID enters.*

Sam: Davey! Where have you been?

David: Whitechapel Art Gallery and the Public Library next
door, that is to say if one should call them that. The Art
Gallery contained no art and the Public Library contained no
public, just one or two down-and-outs reading the long
newspapers in the racks. *(MR SEGAL whispers to DAVID)*

Mr Segal: David, listen to me, try and be a good boy for a
change, your father is dying.

David: So are we all, all the time.

Sam: Stop whispering, Mr Segal. It's not good manners.

David: Anyway, he looks perfectly all right to me.

Sam: Mr Segal, do me a favour, leave me here with my boy for a
moment; I want to talk to him. *(MR SEGAL is looking over
the wall and is shouting at the children who have been
making a little noise)*

Mr Segal: Go on — do us a favour — play somewhere else, little
ruffians. *(He goes off in their direction)*

Children: *(off)* Silly Solly Segal — nose like an eagle — eyes like
two jelly-fish — teeth like a weasel... *(Their voices disappear
in the distance) (DAVID walks round the stage: he stretches
his arms exuberantly but he is nervous)*

Sam: Na Davey, what can I say to you? All these years I wanted
you to work in the market with me, then I told myself "Don't
worry, Sam, he's looking for something better" well what are
you going to do? No more pie in the sky. You've got to support
your mother now.

David: Oh, what can I do?

From *The Hamlet of Stepney Green* (1956)

141

SAM: You'll have to work.

DAVID: Why should I work when I've got my health and strength? The thought of having to spend the rest of my life looking at the heads of herrings and the heads of hungry people makes me sick.

SAM: What do you think singers see? Stop dreaming and settle down.

DAVID: *(swings around the stage)* I want to be a singer — I want to be a king — to be looked at — to be looked up to. I want people to nudge each other as they pass and say "Look! there goes David Levy the most famous fabulous singer in the world". I want to hear my voice blaring from the record shops as I whizz by in my Jaguar. I want to switch on the radio any time and any day and hear my voice on records.

SAM: Why, Davey? Why have you got these crazy ideas? Who do you take after?

DAVID: I feel good when I'm singing.

SAM: But I'm going to die — who'll look after you?

DAVID: Don't worry about me — I'll be all right, and don't keep on saying you're dying. Whatever happens, though I won't work down the lane — I refuse I won't I'll...

SAM: It's not natural — already you're 22 — other boys grow out of these mad ideas already. Other people have only joy from their children — I have a pain in my heart — just my luck. You have no trade — no profession — you're not interested in politics and you drift from job to job. All this has got to stop — I'm a dying man — don't argue.

DAVID: I'm fed up round here. I'm bored. Nothing happens except to other people in the papers. It was bad enough before we got television — now it's worse — everyone sleeps all the time — no one's got any life now — if they gave me a chance on the tele I'd wake them all up — I'd stun them — I'd be the greatest thing don't ya see I want to make people happy — I'VE GOT TO MAKE them listen — they'd love me.

SAM: And they call me delirious. What do you want? Look! Tell me — between you and me — I told you the facts of life,

142

didn't I? Well, you owe me something in exchange — I helped to make you well, don't make any more nonsense — tell me.

DAVID: You made me all right — you made me what I am. Aren't you proud of me? I know you are deep down. What do you want me to do? Be honest.

SAM: To settle down — take over the business — marry a nice girl.

DAVID: What, and then have a complicated son like me? Something's wrong and you know it. You haven't really been a success because you don't really want me to end up in the market like you — come on, own up.

SAM: Naturally I expect you to improve — big business man with a wonderful education.

DAVID: You admit, then, you don't want me to have the same life as yourself? (*SAM cannot reply*) It didn't turn out too well, so surely you don't want me to fail do you? (*SAM cannot reply*) Well, do you? See — you don't know what to say.

SAM: All I can say is that I don't know where you come from.

DAVID: Singing makes me feel safe — it'll give me a place in the world.

SAM: What a complicated boy I have to turn out!

DAVID: When I sing I feel free.

SAM: Davey — all this nonsense has got to stop.

DAVID: Pipe down — you're dying, remember — we've been through this so many times.

SAM: What a way to treat a father; especially on his death-bed. (*He almost cries*)

DAVID: Sorry, Dad — but you've been on this death-bed so many times before — don't blackmail me — anyway why do you want to bequeath me the things you hated — and I know you hated — you told me you hated — as often as you said you were going to kick the bucket — tell me that?

SAM: I shall die a very confused man now — I don't know what I mean.

DAVID: Say that again and anyway even if you were dying how do you do — I'm dying also — dying to be famous and express myself — you'll be all right —. It's me I'm worried about — but just give me a chance. Give me time and I'll make you proud of me. So long, I'll be seeing you. I've got some mirror exercises to do. See you soon.

SAM: I wonder. *(DAVID goes off. SAM laughs ironically. HAVA enters the garden and BESSIE enters from the house)*

BESSIE: Sam, Sam. What's the matter with you? Have you been lecturing my Davey again? You'll upset him. *(Her hair is dyed blonde; she is trying to look ten years younger, and uses cosmetics profusely)*

SAM: Bessie, please believe me; I tell you I'm very ill, please believe me.

BESSIE: If you say so who am I to argue. You were very ill last year and the year before that and the year before that; it's funny but every time it becomes July, you become ill as regular as clockwork. Just when everyone starts to think about holidays, he gets ill. What's the matter? Why don't you say that you don't want to take me to the seaside? And if you're so ill why won't you let me call for a doctor?

SAM: Oh, leave me alone, what do you care? You'll be able to play on your little spirit board and talk to me next week.

BESSIE: Look, Sammy, please be a good boy; it's so hot and I'm expecting Mr and Mrs Stone to tea.

SAM: How is the new Jewish Spiritualist Synagogue doing? Are you playing to full houses? Who ever heard of it? Yiddisher Spiritualism! Is there anyone there? Is it you up there Moishe: send me down a dozen pairs of nylons and five pounds of smoked salmon; I should like to see you all tapping the table for a change, instead of each other.

BESSIE: You disgust me, you old fool; and if you're going to die, please do it before tea-time because I've got a spongecake in the oven. *(She exits into the house) (HAVA comes forward)*

SAM: *(does not see her)* Eh? Sammy? So this is what you made of your life; well, maybe it's just as well; think how difficult it would be to part for ever if you loved each other.

144

Hava: Don't worry, Mr Levy, try and go to sleep.

Sam: Who's that? (*He sits up*) Oh, it's you, Hava. Looking for your Dad?

Hava: No, I just looked in. Miriam wasn't in.

Sam: Oh, God, life was a mistake; it shouldn't have been given to us, we didn't deserve it. The cockroaches deserve life more than human beings.

Hava: Don't you love each other any more?

Sam: No, no more.

Hava: Did you ever love each other?

Sam: Yes; I tell you this as a warning. I was on a steamer going to Southend for the day; she was sitting on the top deck in a white calico dress and her lovely black eyes smiled down at me, oh, so expressive. Two years later we got married, and moved to this house and after Davey was born we went shopping and bought twin beds. What went wrong? I shall never know! There is too much in life, too much to learn, not enough time. Too many problems to be solved. It's too late, now. (*DAVID comes back into the garden; his mood has changed*)

Hava: Look, there's David. (*DAVID ignores her completely as if she doesn't exist. SAM continues talking*)

Sam: I used to think that the top of my head would blow off trying to answer these questions; then one day I thought that I'd grow a new head where these problems would seem like simple sums, nice pieces of cake that you could digest and get rid of easily. Hello, Davey, you met Hava, didn't you?

David: I'm sorry, Dad, but a person can't help being himself. Oh? Yes, I've seen her around. (*He ignores her*)

Sam: Hava, come here, you've met my boy Davey, haven't you?

Hava: Well, we never quite — (*HAVA offers DAVID her hand and he shakes it limply and then continues to ignore her. She just does not exist in DAVID's eyes. SAM pulls DAVID close and ruffles his hair. HAVA walks around the garden sometimes looking at them and sometimes looking at and sniffing the flowers.*) Don't mind me.

145

SAM: We shouldn't argue, you and I. I've always loved you. You were all I really ever lived for; part of that lovely dream that slipped through my fingers. I'm sure you'll find yourself, one day, and when you do remember me and all the others who never got anywhere. *(DAVID is sad)* Come on, Davey, pull yourself together; liven up, sing. Say all those crazy things I used to chastise you for saying. Spout all the things you read from books and heard from your strange friends. I want to change everything. I want something new to happen. I want to lose all sense of order, so that I'll be prepared for my new existence if there is one! Everyone where I'm going may be like you; I want my son to vouch for me in the unaccustomed darkness. Come on, Davey, "Hurrah, Hurrah", come on, darling, spout poetry, sing, shout, come on, Davey. *(He claps his hands — and so does HAVA. SAM has got out of bed again)*

DAVID: *(shouting)* Listen, everyone; listen, folks. This is David Levy speaking, your master of ceremonies, your own prince of song, a prisoner of seasons, a disciple of dust. I fell out of the sky and a name fell upon me, and I was called Levy and now for a time I answer to that. My old man is going to die and so are we all before your very eyes.

HAVA: Come on, Davey, sing. I like hearing your voice.

SAM: Come on, Davey, sing.

DAVID: No! Not now. I want to speak. Tonight, friends, I'm going to launch my father into space.

SAM: Halleluia, I'm a bum; Halleluia, bum again; halleluia, give us a handout to revive us again. *(There is a general commotion in the neighbourhood; irate voices are heard and the CHILDREN have come on the stage and are standing around happy and delighted.)*

DAVID: This is David Levy speaking to you; I'm consigning my father to you, oh mighty dead, he is a king if ever there was one, first because he is my father, and then he is king of the herrings; to you, oh mighty dead, to you, all you billions and billions of dead who have passed this way over the earth, since it shot off from the sun, accept my father, a humble novice in this game of chance, in this maze of existence, look after him for my sake. *(MR SEGAL enters)*

146

MR SEGAL: What on earth are you doing? Sam, get back into bed at once, do you want to catch your death of cold?

HAVA: Daddy, please; don't interfere.

SAM: I'll die from what I choose. I'll die from playing blind man's buff if I feel like it; it's a free country; come on, kiddies, come and play with me.

MR SEGAL: *(to HAVA)* You shouldn't have let him, anyway what are you doing now? *(He sees DAVID)* Don't you get mixed up with him, that's all I ask. Haven't I been a good father? Don't the things that I tell you count?

HAVA: Oh, Daddy, shut up, shush... *(The CHILDREN are reluctantly approaching SAM, who is beckoning them)*

SAM: Go on, sing and dance, show me how to do it. *(The CHILDREN move around in a circle)* What games shall we play? What songs do you know? *(The CHILDREN move around in a circle)*

CHILDREN: There were three crows sat on a stone.
Fal, la, la, la, lal, de.
Two flew away and then there was one.
Fal, la, la, la, lal, de.
The other crow finding himself alone,
Fal, la, la, la, lal, de.
He flew away and then there was none,
Fal, la, la, la, lal, de.

(They continue dancing around like this and SAM and HAVA join in with them. They become quieter and dance on like this whilst DAVID looks at them and sings simultaneously)

DAVID: Sky, sky, the children cry,
Where do we go to when we die?
What are we doing in this dream?
Sky, sky, the children scream,
Sky, sky, the children scream,
Life is nothing but a dream,
A game of dancing in a ring,
Sky, sky, the children sing.
Sky, sky, the children sing,
Who'll be beggar? Who'll be king?

Let's dance for joy, let's sing and leap,
And comfort everyone who weeps.
Sky, sky, the children weep,
Why are we falling fast asleep?
We'll play this game until we die.
Sky, sky, the children cry.

CHILDREN: He flew away and then there was none;
Fal, la, la, la, lal, de.
(*The CHILDREN clap and SAM is encouraging them.
SEGAL is still trying to get him back into bed, without
success*)

HAVA: (*to DAVID*) That was very nice, you can really sing.

DAVID: Who are you? Oh, yes! Thanks. (*He smiles and moves
away, disinterested before she can reply*)

HAVA: My — I'm — Hava... You've got a lovely — voi... Oh,
dear, what a life!

SAM: Come on, now, ring-a-ring-a-roses. (*He and DAVID now
form a circle with the CHILDREN*) (*HAVA stands sadly near
her father, watching*) Ring-a-ring-a-roses, a pocket full of
posies,
Usher, usher, we... all fall... DOWN. (*They all fall on the
grass, and DAVID and the CHILDREN manage to get up,
but SAM can't manage it*)

DAVID: Come on, Dad, come back to bed. (*SAM pushes him away
with a silent gesture of his hands, crawls over to a rose-bush.
He plucks enough and then he staggers to his feet; he stoops
and gives a flower to each child, one to DAVID, which he puts
into his lapel, and one to HAVA*)

SAM: Go on now, kiddies, hide-and-seek, now we are playing
hide-and-seek; run away and hide; run away, quickly get
away, hide-and-seek. (*He is shouting at them and the
CHILDREN quickly run from the garden*) (*DAVID and HAVA
help SAM back into bed. SAM settles back and is calm again.*)
Now, seriously, let's face facts, what's going to happen to you,
Davey?

MR SEGAL: What do you mean? God forbid if anything happens
to you, he'll take over the stall; he's bound to.

DAVID: Here we go again. Oh well, I know — I've had it — I'm caught. What do you want of me? Bang go my dreams, my lovely dreams, my prospects.

MR SEGAL: Now he's beginning to see sense. By the way, Davey, have you met my daughter...?

DAVID: Yes. We met.

SAM: Mr Segal, would you mind not interfering in my business; you've done so long enough. (*SEGAL is offended and sits back and reads a newspaper, and through the next scene he is very interested, though every time DAVID or SAM looks his way he, quickly reverts to the paper.*)

HAVA: Well, I'll go now. Goodbye, Mr Levy. Goodbye, Davey. Don't worry, everything will be all right.

SAM: Goodbye, darling... What a lovely g...

DAVID: Oh? Oh, goodbye... I'm sure it will. (*HAVA kisses her father on the cheek and goes sadly off*)

SAM: You are covered, Davey boy, I hope you realise that; I've got a special endowment for you. When I die you will get two hundred pounds. Well? You don't seem very eager, don't you want the money?

DAVID: I don't want that sort of money. Anyway, what can you do with two hundred pounds?

SAM: You can build up the business into a really posh layout; or you can take a world trip before you begin.

DAVID: Don't make me laugh, a world trip? You're living in the past. All I could do is buy a motor-scooter or eight new suits. (*The stage is slowly getting darker, slightly*) Look, Dad, no one thinks for one moment that you're going to die. Nobody takes you seriously; everybody believes that you'll outlive the lot of us.

SAM: Listen Davey. A word of advice. Don't settle for second best like your mother and I did. Marry a girl who shares your interests, so that when the love of passion cools down, the love of admiration and real friendship flares up and compensates; and then you have the deep ties that can never be broken, not by anything. Do you understand what I mean?

DAVID: Of course.

SAM: Then promise me you'll try your best.

DAVID: Oh, Dad, why do you think...? Oh, never mind, I'll try.

SAM: Will you stay here when I'm dead?

DAVID: I don't know, I suppose so.

SAM: Good boy, but are you sure? I mean, be careful of your mother — she'll kill you with her love for you.

DAVID: Make up your mind — now I decide to stay you start getting cold feet.

SAM: I've got more than cold feet I've got the screaming willies and the heeby-jeebies multiplied together. There's a great wail leaving my soul as if my body was the great wailing wall. *(Enter BESSIE with MR and MRS STONE)*

MR STONE: How are you, Sam?

SAM: Not so bad. How are you?

MR STONE: Mustn't grumble.

SAM: Why not? *(There is a shaking of hands all round and the guests sit down)* How are you Mrs Stone?

MRS STONE: All right, thank you. How are you, Bessie?

BESSIE: Don't ask me; what with one thing and another I don't know if I'm coming or going. *(She exits into the house. MRS STONE nods continuously like a Chinese mandarin)*

MRS STONE: Well, Sam, how are you feeling? Bessie tells me you have a chill.

SAM: The chill is gone, thank God; I'm going to follow it.

MRS STONE: Good, good. How are you, David? Working?

DAVID: I'm fine. I've got a job circumsizing yiddisher mice.

MRS STONE: Sounds an interesting job.

MR STONE: He's having you on. *(BESSIE returns with a tray of tea things)*

BESSIE: Take no notice of him, Mrs Stone what a life I have with that boy, no tongue can tell; there's no house like this, not another house in the world like this; all we do is argue. Oh

150

come on, let's all have a nice cup of tea. *(They are all seated around the small garden table that has a striped coloured umbrella above it. They sip tea and talk)*

MR STONE: What do you think of the political situation, Sam?

SAM: What about it? *(He shrugs)*

MRS STONE: How's Lottie, Mrs Levy?

BESSIE: She's very well, when I heard last; she's living in Leeds — of course you know. He's a school teacher up there; so I mustn't grumble. He looks after her even if he isn't a yiddisher feller. Beautiful weather we are having. How's business, Mr Stone?

MR STONE: Mustn't grumble.

SAM: Why not?

MR STONE: The taxi game never changes; too many new boys taking it up; they all think it a cushy life; they'll learn soon enough. I also stand down the Lane on Sundays now and again. I'm what you might call a purveyor of bad taste; anything that I can get my hands on I sell; you know, those horrible plaster dogs and boys eating cherries, balloons, — little men running up sticks, nonsense. Give the British public something to waste money on and they cry for the opportunity. Alabaster saints and plaster ducks, oh, horrible. Mustn't grumble. Did you hear that fight the other night, Sam? Gerry Freed, the yiddisher boy from Brooklyn, got knocked out in the first round by the coloured boy. I told you so.

SAM: I don't listen to boxing any more.

MR SEGAL: He reads the Bible instead. Nearly all day, nearly all night.

MR STONE: And how are you, Mr Segal?

MR SEGAL: Why should I complain? I've got such good children: my son sends me fifty dollars a month from the States and my girl looks after me like a little mother. Have a cigar? *(He hands one to MR STONE and one to SAM)* He sends these to me from America; I feel like a millionaire; still, why not? Didn't I slave long enough for them?

151

MRS STONE: I wish I had some children to appreciate me. I would appreciate that. *(She looks at MR STONE and he pinches her cheek)*

MR STONE: *(sings)*
When your hair has turned to silver
I will love you just the same;
I will always call you sweetheart.
It will always be your name...

DAVID: Oh, Christ!

MR STONE: What's the matter, David? Don't you like my voice? I had a good voice when I was younger; I once won an amateur competition at the Troxy. Anyway, Sam, what's all this about you reading the Bible in your old age?

SAM: There are a couple of reasons why I started to re-read the Bible; first, I wanted to get what you may call a little spiritual comfort; I wanted to understand life a bit more.

MRS STONE: Anyway, Alf *(to her husband)*, what's wrong with the Bible? Intelligent men read it, educated men, I can tell you that; more people should read it; there wouldn't be so many blackguards about.

DAVID: I am a blackguard and I read the Bible.

MR SEGAL: What's this? What's this? Sam, do you hear that? Your own son said he was a blackshirt. You should be ashamed of yourself. (*BESSIE hands him some cake.*)

SAM: Shut up, Davey, take no notice of him everyone, he's trying to assert himself. Well, where was I? Oh, yes. I wanted to clear up a few points that worried me since I was a child. Now, Adam and Eve had only two sons: Cain and Abel; as you know Cain killed Abel. Well, how did future generations come about? Who did Cain sleep with, I ask you. Incest, you might think. I looked it up yesterday and found that Cain went out into the land of Nod, and knew his wife.

ALL: Land of Nod?

SAM: Yes, the land of Nod. *(They all look at MRS STONE who has been nodding all the time)*

MRS STONE: Why are you looking at me? What have I got to do with it?

152

SAM: You see, it's allegorical.

MR STONE: Sounds like a sweet.

SAM: That's paragorical. Listen, don't interrupt; well, who was this wife that he suddenly started to know, who wasn't even created? Where did she come from? Was she a monkey? So what can you believe? Then there's the Talmud, the Apocrypha, the story of Lilith, Susanna and the Elders; you see, none of you have heard of these things. This is the age of the specialist; you've got to specialise, otherwise where are you? Has anyone here heard of the Tarot cards? The Kaballa? *(They all shake their heads)*

MRS STONE: Kaballa, Shmaballa, leave us alone. What's the matter, Bessie? Is he delirious? Bessie, I bought a lovely halibut for tomorrow's dinner. Well, Bessie, how are you keeping?

BESSIE: I've got a bit of fibrositis as usual, the same as yesterday.

MR STONE: Yes, Sam, the world's in a terrible state.

DAVID: Well — Halibuts are in a terrible state — and the world's suffering from fibrositis — my old man's dying to die — my mother's got a Kaballa in the oven — all right with the world — please nod by you — the world's turning and I'm yearning to sing through the streets about my sadness and joy — Goodbye — so nice to have met you — don't call again. Charming nice son you have — tata — what a world! What a crazy, beautiful world! *(He goes off humming and BESSIE chases off after him)*

BESSIE: *(off)* Davey — wrap up warm it's getting chilly. *(MR and MRS STONE get up and make ready to go. BESSIE comes on again)*

MR STONE: Well, Sam, take it easy; I wish you better.

MRS STONE: So long, Sammy, see you some more. Goodbye, Mr Segal, take care of yourself.

BESSIE: Wheel him back into the house, Mr Segal. Don't listen to him. *(BESSIE exits with MR and MRS STONE)*

SAM: Goodbye goodbye. Thank God for that. *(It is getting very dark now)*

153

MR SEGAL: Shall I wheel it in now; you heard what she said?

SAM: Mr Segal, never be intimidated by a woman; leave me here for another half an hour. I want to see the first star in the sky. Thank you, go on now, go inside, leave me alone; we'll play cards later.

MR SEGAL: You know what I miss? A good game of chess; there are no chess players left in the East End. Mr Solomans and me were the champion players; I haven't played since he died last year. Where has Bessie gone?

SAM: To the spiritualist meeting with the others; they want to talk to the dead; they are fed up with the living.

MR SEGAL: *(puffing on his cigar)*: Madame Blavatsky was an intelligent woman; I saw her once.

SAM: So was Ouspensky.

MR SEGAL: Rasputin was a terrible man; evil and hypnotic.

SAM: So was Ivan.

MR SEGAL: So was Stalin.

SAM: So they say.

MR SEGAL: So was Bakunin.

SAM: So was Trotsky.

MR SEGAL: Oh, no, Trotsky was a wonderful man.

SAM: Lenin was a wonderful man.

MR SEGAL: Kropotkin was a wonderful man.

SAM: My father was a wonderful man.

MR SEGAL: Gorki was a wonderful man, my father knew him.

SAM: Tolstoi was a wonderful man, my father never knew him. Mr Segal, do you think that there's going to be a war?

MR SEGAL: What do you mean? The war never finishes; the independent struggles of the individual to break his chains; the workers themselves — and the distribution of property. In the words of our greatest comrade, "Comrades, down with politics".

SAM: What's the name of this greatest comrade?

MR SEGAL: Izzy Cohen; you know him. He's a furrier, lives in Commercial Street. *(SEGAL exits and HAVA enters)*

HAVA: Hello, Mr Levy, have you seen my father?

SAM: He's gone inside for a moment. Is it urgent?

HAVA: No. I've just come to take him home. How are you feeling?

SAM: Not too good, but I'll be better presently. *(He seems to be in pain)*

HAVA: You rest. It'll do you the world of good.

SAM: Do me a favour, Hava. Try to get to know my son.

HAVA: I would love to. We used to play together, but since I came back he looks right through me. I think he's a very nice boy and I wish he would speak to me; he probably thinks I'm still a child.

SAM: Maybe it's a natural reaction against women; after all, he hasn't exactly a good impression of married life. Listen, I'm going to die.

HAVA: Going to die? Please, Mr Levy, don't speak that way; you scare me. It's a lovely day, all the flowers are out...

SAM: Listen, be a good, sensible girl I've had my time and I'm going to die — what's more natural than that? Face facts — you're a woman now.

HAVA: What will happen to David?

SAM: Try to get to know him — he's my big worry.

HAVA: If only he'll let me — I don't want to push myself — he's too busy with worrying about his voice.

SAM: But I thought you liked his voice.

HAVA: I do — I love it but he doesn't like me. What can I do?

SAM: Take your time — there isn't a woman yet born who let her quarry slip through her fingers — encourage him to sing if you want to — but bring him down to earth — tempt him — you're just the girl he needs.

HAVA: Do you think so?

SAM: Sure you're such a lovely girl — so attractive and good-natured — ideals are very fine but they don't keep you warm in bed — he'll fall — be patient.

HAVA: Do you really think so? Anyway — I'm not that hard up — plenty more fish in the sea.

SAM: Yes, but not such a lovely red herring like my Davey — anyway do your best.

HAVA: I'll try.

SAM: Promise? For my sake — his sake — your sake?

HAVA: I promise. You sleep now, Mr Levy you'll feel much better tomorrow, you'll see. I must go now and find my Dad — are you comfortable? Can I get you something?

SAM: No, no, no. There's a good girl. Go now, you're an angel.

HAVA: Are you sure you don't need anything? (*SAM shakes his head. HAVA goes off into the house*)

SAM: Little girls are so lovely — so gentle and kind. Lots of things I need, darling, but it's too late to think about them now. (*The CHILDREN start to sing again: their voices are much slower and slightly off key*)

CHILDREN: (*off*)
On the hill there stands a lady,
Who she is I do not know.
All she wants is gold and silver,
All she wants is a fine young man
(*DAVID jumps over the garden fence and stands inconspicuously among some flowers*)

DAVID: (*sings*): On the hill there stands a lady,
Who she is I do not know.
All she wants is gold and silver,
All she wants is a fine young man.
On the hill there stands a lady
Who she is I do not know,
I have seen her often lately,
In the sun and in the snow.

156

All she wants is golden rings and silver,
So I heard the little children sing,
She must know that I am not a Rockefeller,
I am skint and haven't got a thing.
All she wants are diamonds, and all she wants are sables,
All she wants are all the things that I could never
Hope to give her —
When I stretch my hands to reach her,
Stretch my longing hands to reach her,
The city throws its lonely streets at me.

SAM: It got dark suddenly, as if the sun fell like a stone; I thought I heard someone singing. The world would be very dark if there wasn't any light; that goes without saying. Ah, there it is, the evening star. Starlight, starbright, first star I've seen tonight, wish I may, wish I might, grant this wish. *(He closes his eyes and makes a wish and then he opens them again and fumbles in the bedclothes for a cigarette; he lights the cigarette, puffs at it for a few moments and then throws it away. DAVID picks up the cigarette and smokes it.)* A funny thing has happened to me, I know it. I've been poisoned.

DAVID: Poisoned?

SAM: My heart is jumping, all the bitterness of years I can taste in my throat. I've been poisoned by someone or something. What's the odds? By my life or my wife. But my wife was my life; so my life poisoned me, so my wife poisoned me.

DAVID: She? Poisoned him? My mother?

SAM: What do I care? I don't want to live another day; die quietly, Sam, let no shame come on the name of Levy. Who'll miss me anyway? Caruso is dead and Chaliapin is dead; Melba is dead; Stepney Green is dead; Whitechapel is dead. What am I waiting for? Whatever became of Whitechapel? Teeming with people, so gay, so alive... where are they? Where are the old men with the long white beards, where are the women selling beigels? Where are the young fellers following the young ladies along the Waste? Everyone I ever loved is dead, everything that was any good is dead, has been murdered. *(DAVID hurriedly walks across the back of the garden and goes into the house)* Our standards are lowering;

everything is dead and being put into tins, smaller and smaller, goodbye cabbages, goodbye oranges, goodbye silver fishes; everything is in tins and compressed, frozen and chopped up. We are being dried and turned inside out and we are watching ourselves in this process on little silver screens; I may as well be dead. *(DAVID returns to the garden and is about to go over to his father when he decides against this and takes his previous position)* Mumma? Yes, I can hear you. Speak louder. How are you? *(He is sitting up and staring at the air)* I am cold. Oh, rock me, Mumma, I am tired. Oh Mumma, Mumma, hold me. Where are you? Let me see, oh there you are. Come closer, closer, stand by the candles. You haven't changed. There is a long river that flows from the Minories, under Tower Bridge; it flows into the sea, but it doesn't lose itself; it flows all over the long ocean and I am swimming so easily along it to you. To Russia, where you are standing, smiling at me; oh, Mumma, how lovely you look I — *(He climbs out of bed)* What's up with you, Sam? Your mind's wandering. You should be ashamed of yourself, calling for your mother. *(He walks about the stage deliriously and by the time the next speech ends he is slumped across the bed)* Oy, Mumma, I remember how you used to swing me, right up into the sky, and then down to the ground... I remember you singing... *(He sings)*

(Note: song will be sung in Russian or Yiddish) (singing):
Go to sleep, mine baby, go to sleep.
Whilst the stars above begin to peep,
Through the window of heaven, angels watch over you.
Roshinkes mit mandlen. Shluf mein kindele, shluf...

Oh, Mumma, look. I am crying on your apron. Let me sleep against you. I love the smell of your clothing. Oy, what can you do when you die alone? *(He is lying spreadeagled across the bed looking upwards. DAVID rushes to him)*

DAVID: Dad, listen to me; you are not alone.

SAM: If you die alone, wherever you are, what can you do?

DAVID: *(shakes him)* I tell you, Dad, you are not alone. Oh, can't you hear me?

SAM: Even if fifty people surround your bed, you die alone.

158

DAVID: Dad, Dad, you are not alone. This is David. I'm with you.

SAM: For when the eyes close no-one can go into that total darkness with you.

DAVID: I'm with you. Listen, Dad, I love you.

SAM: So here goes Sam Levy —poisoned by his life; a *smaltz* herring dealer of Wentworth Street mourned by his d-ial-ect-ical daughter and by his crazy singing son. Oy, oy *Shema Yisroel* — Dear Mother keep me warm. *(He dies)*

DAVID: *(rushing round the stage)* Hi, there, everyone; come out, come out, my father is dead; he is dead; he's been poisoned; for God's sake let's have some light, lights — lights... *(All the lights go full on. SEGAL and HAVA rush onto the stage. DAVID weeps on his father's body. SEGAL rushes to DAVID and pulls him away. HAVA clutches at DAVID's sleeve)*

DAVID: Who are you? What do you want? *(HAVA runs off the stage crying. SEGAL and DAVID stand together looking at SAM's body, unable to move. The CHILDREN are heard singing quietly)*

CHILDREN: Sky, sky the children cry,
Where do we go to when we die?
What are we doing in this dream?
 Sky, sky, the children scream.
SKY: SKY: SKY: SKY: SKY: SKY: SKY: SKY. *(The word becomes louder and louder until it becomes metallic and unbearable)*

———————————

159

from **Enter Solly Gold**

Street scene. Dark stage and simple setting. A row of small houses near Aldgate in London's East End. The set is in a stylised manner and the interior can be seen as well as the exterior. When action takes place in a particular house or area — that place is simply lit up. It is one o'clock in the morning; late summer. A PROSTITUTE stands outside her street door and SOLLY enters. As she sings he sizes her up from afar.

PROSTITUTE (sings): Yours for a short time, how about it honey?
    I'll give you five minutes, if you've got the money.
    You can have me once or have me all night.
    I'm very versatile if the price is right.
    I can be naughty if you pay me cash,
    Now don't be so bashful, come and have a bash.
    If you want what I've got you can have it honey
    I'll give you five minutes if you've got the money.
    (She beckons SOLLY).

SOLLY: Do you mean me?

PROSTITUTE: Why not? I'm not particular. I'll take anyone, as long as they're not jockeys or fishmongers.

SOLLY: What's wrong with jockeys? Some of my best friends...

PROSTITUTE: Whores are not horses. They tend to dig their heels in and treat the bed like a winning post.

SOLLY: What's wrong with fishmongers?

PROSTITUTE: They stink, besides you've got to draw the line somewhere. Come on, don't let's waste time.

SOLLY: Changed my mind, I thought you were fatter.

PROSTITUTE: You don't know what you want — B-off, go on.

SOLLY: But maybe I could stretch a point just this once.

From *Enter Solly Gold* (1964)

PROSTITUTE: Make up your mind or it'll soon be closing time. Now come on, I want cash on delivery.

SOLLY: How much will you charge me to have a chat?

PROSTITUTE: Cut it out. What do you take me for? None of that kinky stuff for me, at least not unless you make it worth my while.

SOLLY: You mean you charge more for talking? Why?

PROSTITUTE: 'Cos I've heard it all before. How much do you think psychiatrists charge for listening? Five quid for five minutes, that's the fixed rate.

SOLLY: I could become a Catholic and they'd listen for nothing.

PROSTITUTE: Take it or leave it, that's the standard charge.

SOLLY: How much do you charge ordinary rate for the ordinary thing?

PROSTITUTE: Three quid and no beating about the bush.

SOLLY: Three quid? You're a profiteer! It was only thirty bob before I left.

PROSTITUTE: You're living in the past, grandad, prices are rising all the time.

SOLLY: Sorry I wasted your time, fact is I've been daydreaming in the middle of the night. I'm flat broke — stony skint — haven't even got a bed for the night — take a look at the soles of my shoes.

PROSTITUTE: You're breaking my heart.

SOLLY: I'm hungry too, haven't eaten for days.

PROSTITUTE: Don't come the old acid with me. You might have heard of sentimental tarts with soppy hearts but yours truly is not like that — times are hard, can't even walk the streets these days. The likes of you should be shot, you've got no morals, no principles, that's your trouble.

SOLLY: Well, this is as far as I can go tonight. *(He sits on his case)*

PROSTITUTE: Your mother should see you now.

SOLLY: My mother! Mum! I can just see her now. I was bad to her but she forgave me — she knew in her heart of hearts that I wanted to help her — she was a famous debutante — Martha Goldberg — I dragged her down and she died in the workhouse — I was just too late — I arrived in my Rolls to take her to the south of England.

PROSTITUTE: Poor boy. *(she shakes herself)* What! You've got the *spiel* all right. You never had a mother. Bet you could melt the heart of a judge. Well, I'm off, I hear the Swedish Navy are pulling in tonight. I hope you don't catch cold and die of pneumonia. So long. *(She goes)*

SOLLY: *(A POLICEMAN enters and watches SOLLY.)* My watch is stopped; wonder if I can pawn it for a few bob? *(He doesn't see the POLICEMAN)* What can I do about kip tonight? Coo, I could kip right here and now I'm so tired — so here we are back in the old country — It's so old it's got one foot in the grave and the other foot's got ingrowing toenails. *(He takes his shoes off and his socks, and starts cutting his toenails. The POLICEMAN who was just about to pounce, has temporarily held off)* What am I gonna do for cash? For the old lolly? Must think of something. But there's one thing I'm sure of — I'm not gonna work — never! Never! — never! *(He stands on the case mocking the Hyde Park orators)* Comrades, if you want work you can have it, as for me, work's too much like an occupation — I've committed no crimes, work is all right for workers, just the job for the working class, but for Solly Gold? There's only one thing he wants, money! And there's only one way he wants to get it — by doing nothing.

Policeman: What do you think you're doing?

SOLLY: *(jumping off case and quickly putting on his shoes)*: Hello, Officer, I remember you from way back. I've just returned from a world trip and do you know — the world's nothing to write home about. They wouldn't let me stay in the States so I returned here to little old England, the greatest little country this side of the Channel.

POLICEMAN: What are you doing?

SOLLY: Isn't it obvious? I'm out here studying the stars — contemplating the infinite.

POLICEMAN: I'll contemplate your what-you-may-call-it if you don't move sharpish. What have you got in that case?

SOLLY: My worldly goods, Officer.

POLICEMAN: You're a saucy bastard, aren't you. Open up.

SOLLY *(opens it)*: One toothbrush, you know for cleaning the teeth. *(Goes through the motions)* One shoebrush for brushing the shoes and one clothesbrush for — Three brushes and a brain, that's all I've got.

POLICEMAN: Where have you come from?

SOLLY: Started on the boat as a dishwasher. By the time I got to Gib I was head steward, but by the time we got to Tilbury, I'd lost everything in a card game. That's the way it goes — up and down — everything's up and down. Ever been to Australia?

POLICEMAN: No.

SOLLY: Do yourself a favour — never go.

POLICEMAN: You said they threw you out of America. Why?

SOLLY: Because I was a member of the blue and white shirts when I was five.

POLICEMAN: What were the blue and white shirts?

SOLLY: How should I know? But I'm going to get into the States, you see. It's my spiritual home. It's dog eat dog there, that's the way I like it.

POLICEMAN: Ain't you no family?

SOLLY: No — no family — no one. *(Sings)*
My mother got struck by lightning,
my father crashed in a plane,
my sister drowned in the Serpentine,
my brother got shot down in Spain.
My cousin died in a madhouse,
my aunt from the sting of a bee,
my uncle jumped off a skyscraper
Oh what's gonna happen to me.

POLICEMAN: I'm on my rounds now and if you're here when I come back you'll be for it. (*POLICEMAN starts to go*) Spiv! Lazy good-for-nothings —

* * *

Solly: I resemble that remark. He should try living on his wits. Believe me it's a damn sight harder than your union would let you work and I'm always on duty twenty-eight hours a day. (*He shouts after the POLICEMAN, then picks up case and moves, but after a few feet he notices light in a window of a tailor's shop: he knocks on the door and falls on his face on the doorstep.*) (*groans*) Oh help me — help me — oh God. (*The TAILOR'S WIFE comes to the door, opens it*)

Rita: (*calls*): Joe! Joe! Come here, someone's in trouble.

Joe: Who isn't? (*He is busy sewing in the interior*)

Rita: But he's on our doorstep.

Joe: So? We won't charge him any rent.

Solly (*desperate*): Help me — oh lady — I'm in terrible trouble. (*He pulls on her skirt and at the same time tries to look up her legs; she doesn't see this*)

Rita: We've got enough of our own, son.

Solly (*loud*): I'm so choked — you're a Jewish woman, aren't you? *Sholem Alecheim.*

Rita: I don't care what your name is — what do you want?

Solly: I'm gonna die — I'm spitting blood. Oh God, that it should happen to me. I'm gonna die.

Joe: Tell him please not on our doorstep — bring him in. (*He is helped inside*)

Rita: Just take it easy, son — try and relax.

Joe: What's he doing out this time of night?

Solly: Oh I'm all water, my legs are just like water — I can't go on. Take me too — kill me also. (*He collapses on the floor. JOE won't leave the machine so RITA pulls him into a chair*) I'm just like water — water.

164

JOE: Rita, fetch him some water.

SOLLY: Haven't you got something a bit stronger?

JOE: Rita, bring him some of that Palestinian wine.

SOLLY: I prefer brandy if you've got it. (*RITA brings him wine*)

JOE: I'm only a poor tailor.

SOLLY: All right, I'll settle for this, I'm not so particular — Oh no, I don't believe it — Becky — where have you gone?

RITA: He's delirious.

SOLLY: Nice wine — thank God I found you up.

RITA: You'll always find us up — he says he can't afford to sleep.

JOE: All right. (*to SOLLY*) So, what's your story?

SOLLY: I can't talk, not yet. Could I have another glass of wine?

JOE: All right. Now listen, you don't feel so well, have a little rest, put your feet up and in two minutes you'll be as right as rain and be able to leave.

RITA: He drives me mad. Joe, can't you see he looks like death, what's the matter, 'fraid you'll lose a few stitches? Work is all he knows. Never marry a tailor. (*She tells SOLLY*) He borrows a few hours from the next day, then a day from the next week and a few weeks from the next year and then he dies owing all that time. (*She goes to JOE*) What's the matter with him, Joe?

JOE: I don't like the look of him.

RITA: He's a Jewish boy, he can't be bad.

JOE: Yeah? What about *Schnorrer* Morry?

RITA: Can't you ever get away from that machine?

JOE: You can grumble; did you ever go without?

RITA: Yes, without you, all my life. I'm married to a sewing machine. (*Returns to SOLLY*) You feeling better, son?

SOLLY: Oh, Becky! Becky! What's the matter with you? Why don't you jump — save the children — the children! Becky, my poor wife — all burned. (*Bursts into tears*)

165

RITA: It's good to tell someone.

SOLLY: I'm a traveller, I only heard before. I live in Glasgow and my wife — oh God rest her soul — died this morning with the children.

RITA: Died? Oh, you poor feller.

JOE: *(leaves machine)*: How?

SOLLY: Oh, it was such a big fire, there were twenty engines, masks they had on. They all got burned to death, my Becky, my little Renee, the twins, Michael and Angela — they were so beautiful. Becky had long black hair — she was a picture.

RITA: The good die young.

SOLLY: Becky tried to save them — she stood on the parapet — with all the children in her arms — little Renee, she was such a lovely dancer — tap and ballet. What can I do?

RITA: Let me make you something to eat.

SOLLY: No, I couldn't, I'm all choked. All right, if you insist, a chicken sandwich with some mustard pickle or some smoked salmon — nothing much — something light. (*RITA goes off to prepare it*) I must go to Glasgow now! I must give them a decent burial.

JOE: Stay here tonight, go tomorrow morning.

SOLLY: I must fly tonight — I'll have to charter a plane.

JOE: Of course, I understand.

SOLLY: I wonder if you could help me? God is good, in times of stress. He sends good friends. Listen I need a few quid for the plane fare — the banks are closed and I must fly tonight.

JOE: How much?

SOLLY: At least twenty-five — yes, that will cover me. Oh, Becky, Becky, by my mother in the grave I'm sorry — forgive me, I tried to be a good husband.

JOE: I'm afraid I can only afford five.

SOLLY: That's no use, make it twenty then.

JOE: What about ten?

166

SOLLY: I'll tell you what, I'll settle with fifteen and try and manage with that.

JOE: All right, fifteen it is!

SOLLY: It's a deal.

JOE: Done! *(They shake hands on it)*

SOLLY: It's only a loan, mind, I'll send it back tomorrow morning.

JOE: There's no hurry, wait till the afternoon. I'll get it. *(SOLLY lies back, smokes and pours himself another drink. JOE meets RITA coming in with sandwiches)* I must be crazy, I'm lending him money.

RITA: It's good to know you've got a heart; he's the first person you've lent money to in the past twenty years.

JOE: Ah well, he's different — you can see it, it's obvious, he's a decent boy in trouble. I'm a good judge of character. *(JOE goes off and RITA brings the sandwiches to SOLLY)*

SOLLY: You're so kind — how can I repay you? *(Stuffs the sandwich into his mouth)* You're too good. I bet no one appreciates you.

RITA: You can say that again. My husband takes me for granted.

SOLLY: When you're dead, then he'll appreciate you, just like me and Becky.

RITA: Try and look forward now, we have to get over things, life goes on.

SOLLY: You're very nice, you're an angel. Has anyone ever told you that? You've got a light in your eyes; does he ever say a kind word to you?

RITA: He hasn't got time. He's not a bad boy exactly, just got no time.

SOLLY: I'd have time for someone like you, I would — you're so nice — oh comfort me — my Becky is dead. *(She pats him on the shoulder and puts her arms around him)* I'm so lonely. *(He pretends to cry and soon he is completely embracing her and touching her hair)* Oh, you're lovely, so lovely, just like my Becky.

RITA: No no. I shouldn't. *(She tries to break away as she realises he is getting amorous)*

SOLLY: Don't leave me — I need you.

RITA: Please, you'd better stop.

SOLLY: You're just my size. I'm mad about you. *(He tries to kiss her but she breaks free and still they speak quietly, urgently)*

RITA: How could you? With your wife just dead? No-one's ever done that to me.

SOLLY: How should I know what I'm doing — I'm so sad and emotional.

RITA: With your wife just dead how could you do it?

SOLLY: Don't tell your husband, he wouldn't understand. I'll come back some other time — I'm mad for you and so unhappy.

RITA: Men make me sick.

SOLLY: Me too. Forgive me, for poor Becky's sake.

RITA: *(wanders off and looks in a mirror)*: How could you do that to me? *(JOE returns)*

JOE: Here you are, fifteen quid.

SOLLY: You're a pal, how can I repay you?

JOE: With money.

SOLLY: I'll be on my way now; God bless you all, my Becky will be so pleased, I mean as she looks down on all this. Goodbye! May you live long and die happy — may you live to be a hundred and three.

JOE: Don't do me no favours.

SOLLY: You're one in a million, both of you. I must fly now. *(He leaves the house and lingers outside, but the light goes off for a moment)*

JOE: Nice feller, ain't it funny how the good always suffer?

RITA: How could he do it to me? *(She rejoins her husband)*

JOE: Well darling, I gave him the money.

RITA: Money? You bloody fool! *Schlemiel.* Why didn't you give me away while you were about it?

JOE: I wish I did.

RITA: Go on, back to your sewing, you silly so and so.

JOE: Why don't you go to bed? I've got a busy night ahead.

RITA: Yes, I'm going to bed and don't wake me up whatever you do — 'cos the answer's no. You've had it from now on; you don't know how to treat a lady — you don't appreciate me. It's alright, people still think I'm attractive. I'm not finished yet. Good night. *(She goes to bed, the tailor continues sewing and the light in the room darkens SOLLY is now seen again, counting the money. The PROSTITUTE comes up to him)*

SOLLY: What happened to the Swedish Navy?

PROSTITUTE: They've got an attack of German measles on board. Bang goes another night's business. I'll have to sleep. My my, you've got a wad there. I'm in the wrong racket.

SOLLY: How much you charge for all night?

PROSTITUTE: Special rates for nightwork — time and a half.

SOLLY: Do me a favour. I want it cut price. How much?

PROSTITUTE: A tenner.

SOLLY: Come off it, I'm only a poor working man.

PROSTITUTE: Oh alright, nine.

SOLLY: Make it three.

PROSTITUTE: You out of your mind? Don't you know about the cost of living index? Seven pounds ten and that's my final word.

SOLLY: Four pounds ten, on the nose.

PROSTITUTE: You'd auction your own mother all right, five quid and not a penny less.

SOLLY: Right, it's a deal. *(They shake on it)*

PROSTITUTE: Let's go.

SOLLY: You're not as fat as I would like but you can't pick and choose all your life. *(They exit into her door and the stage darkens completely now — there is a passage of time and the stage lightens again and it is dawn — a cock is heard crowing and SOLLY comes out of the PROSTITUTE's door, yawns and does some exercises.)* A cock crowing? In Whitechapel? Impossible. *(It crows again. He looks over a fence beside a third house)* Chickens — that's handy. Come on you pretty little darlings — come and get stuffed. Oh boy, that takes me back... chicken soup, stuffed neck, chopped liver, giblet pie. There's one, two, three, five, eight, eleven birds in all, and one lovely rooster — beautiful bird. Looks as if you've had a heavy night like me. Never mind — I'll cut your throat and then you can have a long sleep and then I'll flog you and your girlfriends down the lane. *(He is about to climb over the fence when an OLD LADY comes out of the house with some food for the chickens)*

WOMAN: What do you want? *(He jumps back quickly but soon relaxes)*

SOLLY: I want you. I'm the bird inspector.

WOMAN: Bird inspector? What do you want? Where are you from?

SOLLY: *(more to himself):* As a matter of fact I've been inspecting a bird all night. I'm from the Ministry of Agriculture and Poultry; I've been inspecting your birds.

WOMAN: What's wrong with my birds?

SOLLY: What's right with them? They're having a nervous breakdown. This is a serious business.

WOMAN: Please sir, I can't help it; since my husband died I've been struggling to carry on alone.

SOLLY: Your husband dead?

WOMAN: Yes, a month ago, did you know him?

SOLLY: Of course I did, who didn't.

WOMAN: Who didn't know my Hymie? Who didn't know him and love him?

SOLLY: Wonderful Hymie, with the heart of gold. As a matter of fact he owes me some money.

WOMAN: Money? He never owed, anyone.

SOLLY: I mean the government. He never paid his last installment of the Chicken Registration fee. He owed us ten pounds.

WOMAN: Chicken Registration? No, I didn't know — he took care of everything, I'm so lost without him. I'll pay you.

SOLLY: Poor Hymie, the world won't be the same without him.

WOMAN: It's good to talk to you — I haven't spoken to a soul since he died. You make me feel better — I'm glad you liked my husband so much.

SOLLY: *(looking over the fence)*: The birds will have to go of course.

WOMAN: Why?

SOLLY: Neurotic birds are a menace to society — they're totally maladjusted and what's more I'll have to kill them here and now, I'm afraid. And that will of course be another six pounds disposal fee.

WOMAN: Take them, kill them. Who can be bothered feeding them anyway? Who eats eggs since Hymie died? Here, six pounds.

SOLLY: I'm letting you off light — because I like you and Hymie was a friend of mine.

WOMAN: Thank you, thank you — I know, you're very kind. Death is an expensive business — all I've done since my husband died is lay out, lay out.

SOLLY: I hope I'm not leaving you too short.

WOMAN: As my husband always said, you can always find money for bread and coffins.

SOLLY: *(puts away money)* Now please, I will need a sharp razor to cut their throats. *(She goes inside and he jumps over fence and inspects the birds. She returns and hands him a cut-throat razor. He sets to work though we cannot see his hands or the birds, but very soon amidst a flurry of sound and feathers, he emerges with a cluster of dead birds.)*

171

SOLLY: We'll send you receipts.

WOMAN: One minute, do you know anyone who could use some clothes? I've got some, my husband's things, they're in marvellous condition. I can't bear to see them anymore.

SOLLY: I might be able to help you out, let's have a look.

WOMAN: Do me a favour, pull out that trunk. *(He puts the chickens down and pulls out a large suitcase)* Only the best, as you can see take it all.

SOLLY: A Rabbi's clothes? *(He holds up some jackets and trousers and soon lifts out some Rabbi's clothes)*

WOMAN: But you knew my husband was a Rabbi, didn't you?

SOLLY: Who didn't know? From Tel Aviv to Tell me the Tale he was famous — the best Rabbi in the racket. It's just that I didn't think you'd part with such personal items.

WOMAN: You're right, I wouldn't. Don't touch the Rabbi's clothes and his Bible. Take everything else — I can't bear to see them anymore. I must go now and sweep up. Thank you. *(She goes inside)*

SOLLY: These clothes are not worth a light — she must be blind, they're all moth-eaten, but this Rabbi's gear might come in handy — and I hear there are some very hot tales in this black book. Well, Solly boy, you're not doing too bad — last night you had sweet Fanny Adams and this morning you're worth twenty odd nicker, a dozen chickens and this odd clobber. You're in business. *(He kneels down and prays)* Oh, Rabbi Hymie forgive me but I mean well — I'm a bad boy, but I promise to spread love and happiness everywhere I go 'cos money don't bring happiness so I'm gonna take it away from them. *(He puts the clothes and the chickens in his case)* Watch out, world, I'm coming! Hendon! Golders Green! Hampstead Garden Suburb! I'm knocking on your door! *(He does a little dance and some mock prayers)* I'm Rabbi Solomon Goldstone, I'm knocking on your door, with a new kind of religion and a brand new kind of law, if you can't get in heaven, he'll fix it in a flash — I've got the right connections, if you have got the cash. *(He exits hurriedly)*

---

from Returning We Hear the Larks

(Leo the retiring librarian of Whitechapel Library and his conversation with a Bangladeshi girl)

LEO: These streets are holy. Here we defeated Mosley!

ALEYA: Who was Mosley?

LEO: Who was Mosley? He was a racist upper class thug. Haven't you heard about the famous battle of Cable Street? It was a great victory, a turning point.

ALEYA: Did your victory last?

LEO: What lasts? It is 1936. He came with his thugs and tried to march down our streets. The fascists wanted to intimidate the Jews. We were to become the litmus test for the rest of the world. 1936. Look! The kids throwing marbles under the hooves of police horses. Look! My parents standing on the landing of the buildings, banging washing boards, saucepans. "They Shall Not Pass!" We shouted. And we won. Despite a police force protecting those shit-bags. They didn't march through our East End.

ALEYA: No-one ever told me the Jews experienced prejudice.

LEO: Prejudice was invented for us. These streets. These teeming streets. Almost 200,000 souls were crammed into just one square mile. Now everyone has gone. Maybe there's just a thousand of us left. I'm almost the last Jew. They will carry me out and plant me in Plashet Grove, beside her.

ALEYA: My parents came from Rawalpindi. Where did your parents come from?

LEO: From pogrom.

ALEYA: Pogrom? Where's that?

From *Returning We Hear the Larks*
(unpublished, performed in Whitechapel Library, 2005)

LEO: Everywhere. Believe it or not, in those days this country welcomed the dispossessed. So their ship came up the Thames and my parents stood on the deck and they saw Tower Bridge with its great arms open. They said it was like a huge mother welcoming them to her bosom. They settled here, near the docks, like all immigrants, needing to feel as close to the old country as possible. This East End. It is like an Olympic torch, handed from one community to the next. First the Huguenots who made lace and started the *schmutter* game. Their church in Brick Lane later became our synagogue. And when we disappeared these streets became your streets. Bangladeshi streets. Our synagogue became your mosque. But who will follow you? The stockbrokers. It will all be gentrified. For those who live and thrive on the sweat of others. If the rich could get the poor to do their dying for them there would be no unemployed in this world.

ALEYA: You are a very bitter man, deep down.

LEO: I like your people taking over these streets. They have become alive again. There is a beautiful symmetry in all these migrations. Community is a wonderful thing.

ALEYA: Community can be suffocating. He looks so pale. Isaac Rosenberg. So frail, so vulnerable. I would have loved to have met him, in the flesh.

LEO: Look. I have tried to bring out his lostness. And the unwashed years. We witness the end of days. All gone now. The Jewish tribe. Across the North West Passage to Hendon, Edgware and Totteridge. All gone. To the Essex coast and the graveyard. And now it's your turn. How lucky you are to inherit these streets.

Diaspora

How sad that I have found nowhere,
that I have found no dream,
that I come from nowhere and go nowhere.

This is a land without dream;
an endless landscape.

Beautiful for those who can see their own sunset,
who can grow their own fruit out of their own sweat.
Beautiful for those in their own land,
whose laughter, whose tears soak into their own land.
Whose songs fill the earth and the sky of their own land.

How beautiful to dance and move and live and
dream and die in a country with a dream.

How sad I am that I have found nowhere.
My tears fall into the brick and haste and
death of day to day existence.

This is a country without dream
and no-one notices that I am crying.
By the waters of my own four falling walls I wail.
I hear the trumpets, see the invisible
machines of destruction working in every corner.

How sad that I have found nowhere;
my son has no festival, this sun no ceremony.
How sad that the sea beyond does not lift me,
nor the hills.

From *Barricades in West Hampstead* (1988)

The Lost Love of Phoebe Myers

(A radio play)

Scene One. A dress factory sweatshop in Whitechapel. London's East End. It is 1944. The sound of busy sewing machines. Two girls chat as they work. In the background the radio plays Moonlight Serenade.

PHOEBE: Ten to six! Almost time to go home. Maisie! You awake?

MAISIE: I was dreaming.

PHOEBE: That boy Gerald?

MAISIE: Na! Sent him packing. I was dreaming about being a Land Girl —.

PHOEBE: Maisie! The war's nearly over.

MAISIE: Wish I was in the country. Look at this blinking pile of work!

PHOEBE: Yeah! It never ends. In peacetime there's no work. In wartime there's no unemployment. Life's a strange phenomenon!

MAISIE: Swallowed a dictionary as usual? Oh! Forgot! Boss wants you in his office.

PHOEBE: Hope it's not the sack.

MAISIE: Maybe he wants to give you a rise.

PHOEBE: Maybe he'll make me an experienced machinist at last. Been an improver long enough.

MAISIE: Me too.

PHOEBE: This bloody sweatshop. It's always promises! Promises! Better go, then. Thanks!

MAISIE: Watch out for his wandering hands.

Performed on BBC Radio 4, November 2006

PHOEBE: Don't I know it! The old octopus!

MAISIE: He takes liberties with most of the girls.

PHOEBE: He won't try it on with me, not again.

MAISIE: Careful! I've seen the way he still ogles you with his beady eyes.

PHOEBE: I can look after myself.

MAISIE: If you can't be good by careful. *(They laugh)*

PHOEBE: So? Here I go into the wolf's lair!

More dance music. The sound of busy sewing machines swells. Time passes.

MAISIE: *(To another girl)* Phoebe's come out! She's not crying!

PHOEBE: Why you all looking at me?

MAISIE: So what happened?

GIRLS: Phoebe! Tell us! What happened in there?

PHOEBE: What didn't happen! So I'm standing there as his eyeballs creep — slowly, slowly — all over my body.

VOICES: Great! Did he touch ya? Did he feel you Phoebe?

MAISIE: Filthy old bastard!

PHOEBE: Listen. I'm Mr Gold! Right? *(gruffly, emulating the boss's voice)* Ah! Miss Myers! Sit! Take the weight off your brain. What can I do you for?

PHOEBE: Mr Gold, you sent for me. *(now the boss)* So I did. Don't be fright. That's very nice! Phoebe — May I call you Phoebe?

PHOEBE: You're the boss. *(as boss)* Phoebe! I've been watching you, and I like what I see.

PHOEBE: Thank you. Mr Gold. *(as boss)* Phoebe! Do you know you are a very alluring creature, with those dreamy eyes. I like a well-covered girl, with oomph!

PHOEBE: Thank you Mr Gold. *(as boss)* Phoebe! Please call me Harry. *(as herself)* He's getting very carried away at this point. Why are you panting Mr Gold? Is your collar too tight? Mr Gold! It's time you made me an experienced machinist.

177

(*as boss*) If you're nice to me I'll be nice to you. (*the girls whoop with delight*) Phoebe! I'm making you an experienced machinist. Tomorrow!

PHOEBE: Thank you Mr Gold. (*as boss*) Phoebe! Do you realise how voluptuous and tempting you are.

VOICES: Hiyi! Filthy sod! Did he touch ya? Did his 'ands wander?

PHOEBE: Mr Gold. I must get back to my machine. Then he comes close. "Phoebe! Phoebe!" His nose almost touching my face! He smells of fish. His hands like spiders on my shoulder. His lustful eyes feasting on my flesh!

VOICES: Cor! Wonderful! Dirty dog! (*laugher and grunts*)

PHOEBE: (*as boss*) Got a boy friend yet, Phoebe?

PHOEBE: No thank you Mr Gold. (*as boss*) Then you haven't been naughty recently.

PHOEBE: His hands slowly start to creep towards my tits.

VOICES: Yeah! Phoebe! Go on! Go on!

PHOEBE: Mr Gold! I'm bursting! I must go, quickly, you know where. (*as boss*) Phoebe. Every time I look at you, you drive me nuts! Phoebe! I'm taking you to Blooms next Saturday! For a beautiful supper of salt beef and *latkes*! You'll love it. You'll cry out. More! More!

PHOEBE: Let me go! Please let me go Mr Gold! Let me go or I'll give you nuts! A kick in the balls!

Enormous laughter, then sudden silence.

BOSS: Hello girls! Having a nice chinwag, are we? Back to work! Unless you want your cards! (*sewing machines deafen*)

MAISIE: (*quietly*) Rich. Poor. Young. Old. Goy. Yid. Black. White. English. Chinese. They're all the same. They're only after one thing.

PHOEBE: Oh Maisie! Why are men such beasts? (*they laugh*)

END SCENE.

NEW SCENE. PHOEBE and MAISIE walk home after work

MAISIE: Starving! Can't wait to get home.

PHOEBE: Imagine! A great wedge of cheddar on hot *chola*, smothered with butter. Bananas and cream for afters! This bloody war!

MAISIE: It's nearly over thank God. East End's a graveyard. Peace can't come soon enough!

The air-raid siren sounds

VOICE: *(Air-raid Warden)* Hey you girls! Don't you know there's a war on? Get yourselves home! Quick as you can.

PHOEBE: Don't get your *kishkers* in a twist! Gerry's not gonna get us this late in the war.

MAISIE: We're not the dying sort.

PHOEBE: Come on Maisie! Move it!

They start running, laughing

MAISIE: Here's my street! Look! Me mum's hanging out of the window. Such a worry guts.

PHOEBE: My mum's worse.

MAISIE: Going dancing tonight?

PHOEBE: Maybe.

VOICE: Maisie? Where you been?

MAISIE: Hello Mum! Coming! Phoebe! Take care. See you later?

PHOEBE: Thanks! For everything!

MAISIE: What's that mean?

PHOEBE: For being such a good pal.

VOICE: Maisie! Don't dawdle! There's an alert on!

MAISIE: My mum won't die of a doodlebug. She'll die of aggravation.

PHOEBE: See you later then.

MAISIE: Don't forget we've both got to meet a nice Jewish boy.

PHOEBE: When kosher pigs fly. But who knows?

MAISIE: Seven o'clock then. The Lyceum.

PHOEBE: Hunky Dory darling. I'll come round.

MAISIE: Goodbye darling.

PHOEBE: Goodbye Maisie!

Maisie enters her house. FADE.

Phoebe's house. Wagner's "Gotterdammerung" plays on the gramaphone.

PHOEBE: *(entering)* Hello Mum! Dad! Love you!

FAY: Expect an answer from him? You'll be lucky.

PHOEBE: There he is again. In front of the long mirror, conducting his usual, invisible orchestra. Clock his ecstatic face! Like he's in another world. Mum, I'm starving!

FAY: Egg and chips. A few jiffs! Come into the kitchen. *(two more explosions, quite close. "Gotterdammerung" swells to climax)*

JOE: Those flying bombs are far too close. Diabolical bastards!

FAY: A *krenk* on Hitler's *kishkers*. How was work?

PHOEBE: The boss tried to take liberties.

FAY: May he lose more blood than sea in the ocean!

PHOEBE: But he promised to make me an experienced machinist.

FAY: But what does he want in return?

JOE: I wonder. *(he laughs)*

FAY: He's a man. What can you expect?

SYLVIE: How fresh did he get? Phoebe! Tell me!

PHOEBE: Hello Sylvie! *(now she returns to the living room)* Give us a kiss, little sis.

SYLVIE: *(short)* Phoebe! Doing my homework.

PHOEBE: I'm not helping you.

SYLVIE: Who wants your help!

PHOEBE: You're my precious little monster. I love you. *(they kiss)*

SYLVIE: I was thinking. If a doodlebug fell on this house I wouldn't have to do homework anymore. *(another explosion)*

Mummy! Hate this. I'm hiding under the table.

JOE: Sylvie darling, the war will be over in weeks.

FAY: I married an impossible optimist.

PHOEBE: An optimist is someone who hasn't heard the bad news.

SYLVIE: I'm an optimist, and I'm going to be an actress when I grow up.

PHOEBE: She said, under the table.

JOE: An actress? Over my dead body!

PHOEBE: Spit when you say that. And turn round seven times.

SYLVIE: Bang! Bang! You're dead.

PHOEBE: Dad! You don't own us. We are on loan to you.

JOE: Fine! I'm gonna loan you both to Mrs Gurevitch next door. *(the music swells)* Oh! This part transports me.

FAY: Not far enough.

JOE: Joseph Myers now takes the rostrum. Below him, waiting for my command an orchestra of one hundred players.

PHOEBE: Daddy darling! You are ridiculous.

JOE: Music soothes the soul.

PHOEBE: Why you playing Nazi music?

JOE: Music is above politics.

PHOEBE: Tell that to Mister Hitler. You are an enigma!

JOE: Give them a good education and they start talking Double Dutch. *(another explosion, Sylvie screams)*

JOE: Darling! Come out and I'll cuddle you. *(Sylvie does)* My little Sylvie! You'll be all right. There! Snuggle in.

SYLVIE: Daddy! You're so lovely and kind and so sweet. Why didn't you do better in life?

JOE: Who knows! I am Mr Myers who missed out. Missed the bus. Missed the train, missed the boat. Mister Myers. Bespoke Tailor. That's me!

FAY: Well, don't miss your dinner. Egg and chips. *Fress*! Feed your faces.

JOE: Music feeds me.

FAY: That's nice. No need to do the washing up.

JOE: I'm just a little tailor with dreams. Got a waistcoat to finish. *(he returns to his sewing machine)* Life's unfair. I am probably the best bespoke tailor in the game. So how much do I earn? One pound fifteen shilling a suit. So how much do they get? Those geezers in Saville Row? Twenty five nicker! I shall now conduct the Boston Symphony Orchestra. *(he puts on "Tchaikovski's 6th")*

FAY: He's stone bonkers. His family warned me...

JOE: This passage! Listen! It makes me cry.

PHOEBE: Look! Actual tears in his eyes.

JOE: I should have been a composer. *(the all-clear sounds)* The all-clear! The best music of all.

PHOEBE: Good! I'm meeting Maisie in an hour.

FAY: Going somewhere nice?

PHOEBE: Lyceum. Maybe.

JOE: Up west? Watch out for villains.

SYLVIE: I'd love to meet a villain. If only I was five years older.

FAY: Don't wish your life away.

PHOEBE: Going upstairs to change. *(Phoebe goes up to her room and starts to make up)* My face! Just look at me! My eyes. Mascara's all wonky. I need some decent lipstick.

SYLVIE: Talking to yourself again?

PHOEBE: Sylvie! I'll kill you; creeping in, like that!

SYLVIE: It's my room as well.

PHOEBE: How are my eyes?

PHOEBE: Beautiful. Like a cow on heat!

PHOEBE: One day I'm going to strangle you.

SYLVIE: Your mascara's a bit smudged. Here. Let me. *(she helps)* There! You look almost human now.

PHOEBE: Thank you, darling.

SYLVIE: Can I use your face powder?

PHOEBE: No!

SYLVIE: Thank you.

PHOEBE: Impossible little horror. Give it back!

SYLVIE Hoping to meet a boy tonight?

PHOEBE: No. A space man!

SYLVIE: Will you let him touch you, after the dance?

PHOEBE: Nobody touches me. What are you talking about?

SYLVIE: You know what I mean? Will he try to fondle your titties?

PHOEBE: You are a disgusting little beast.

SYLVIE: Can I do my eyes?

PHOEBE: No! That's my mascara!

SYLVIE: Phoebe! Please! Please! Let me. Thank you. You're a lovely sister and tonight you will attract the handsome boy of your dreams.

PHOEBE: I don't want a boy.

SYLVIE: I know; you want a man. To thrill you again and again and again. "Oh! Please! No! Don't you dare! Stop it! Don't you dare! — Stop it! Oh no! Oh no! Don't you dare stop it!" *(they both laugh)*

PHOEBE: You are an impossible, filthy little imp, and I love you.

SYLVIE: And I love you Phoebe, with all my heart.

PHOEBE: Give us a cuddle. Lovely. Oh my giddy god. I'm late. Maisie will spiflicate me! I'm off. Tera!

SYLVIE: *(Phoebe races downstairs)* Tell me all about it, later.

PHOEBE: Not on your life! Goodbye! Little monster. *(the street door slams)*

FADE. "Moonlight Serenade" plays.

Phoebe runs through the streets

PHOEBE: *(thoughts)* Maisie'll be at the door. She hates being even one minute late. What a lovely full moon! Hello moon! Please send me a nice young man. Good! Almost there. Maisie's house. *(she stops running)*

Note: this whole scene is played quietly. Phoebe does not cry or scream

PHOEBE: *(puzzlement)* What? Officer! What's the barrier for? What's happened?

POLICEMAN: Sorry miss! You can't go down there.

PHOEBE: My friend Maisie lives in this street. My best friend!

POLICEMAN: Sorry. It was late afternoon when the doodlebug came.

PHOEBE: Flying bomb?

POLICEMAN: Yeah! Terrible carnage.

PHOEBE: But my friend lives here. I must find her.

POLICEMAN: Sorry miss, the whole street's been blown to smithereens! You can't go through this barrier. Sorry!

PHOEBE: Let me go! Am I dreaming this?

POLICEMAN: Wish it were a dream.

PHOEBE: Number thirty three! My best friend. Maisie! *(she runs)*

POLICEMAN: Come back! Hey! You can't go down there!

The wind howls. "Gotterdammerung" climax

PHOEBE: *(shouting)* Maisie! Maisie! *(she runs. The wind howls. Her heartbeat throbs)* She's got to be all right! I know she's all right! Where's her house? Wrong street! Can't be Redmans Road. Where is it? Where's the street? Where's — Maisie?

OLD WOMAN: I knew 'em well. The Goodmans. Lovely family! All gorn.

PHOEBE: Please! Would you please tell me this is not happening.

184

OLD WOMAN: Oh yeah! Saw you often. You was her friend. Yeah! All gorn now. Wiped out! I live next turning. Nothing left here. All gorn! Go 'ome. There's a good girl.

PHOEBE: We were going dancing.

OLD WOMAN: She won't be dancing no more. All gorn. All the houses, all the faces I knew. All gorn.

PHOEBE: Help me someone! Tell me I'm dreaming this.

OLD WOMAN: Here one moment. Dust the next.

PHOEBE: *(almost whispering)* Maisie! Maisie!

"Moonlight Serenade" plays, slowly.

NEW SCENE. Phoebe's bedroom. Phoebe has been in her bedroom for two days. Her family rap on the door.

PHOEBE: Go away!

FAY: Phoebe. Darling. Life goes on.

PHOEBE: Does it. *(more rapping)* Go away.

JOE: Phoebe! You've been in there for two days. You haven't eaten. We've left trays of food outside. Please!

PHOEBE: It's not fair!

JOE: Fair she wants! What's fair?

SYLVIE: Phoebe! It's my room as well.

FAY: Phoebe! Maisie's dead! Nothing can bring her back.

JOE: The moving finger writes and having writ moves on.

FAY: *(quietly)* Shut up Joe!

JOE: Phoebe! I've got a surprise for you. Downstairs.

PHOEBE: Go away!

FAY: Phoebe! I'm staying here until you open the door.

PHOEBE: Alright! You can come in. Just you.

FAY: Thank you. All the others have gone down now.

PHOEBE unlocks the door. FAY enters.

FAY: Phoebe! Here! Lovely *lokshen* soup. Here! Eat!

PHOEBE: Soup! Your answer to everything! How could she die? How could she do that to me?

FAY: Phoebe! Life goes on.

PHOEBE: Where does it go? You and your Jewish homilies.

FAY: Have some soup, come downstairs, and have a good cry.

PHOEBE: Mum! The pain's too much for tears.

FAY: Phoebe! I also carry pain. We all do. You must go out.

PHOEBE: Please leave me alone.

FAY: Go dancing. Go for Maisie.

PHOEBE: Never! Never! *(END SCENE)*

NEW SCENE. The crowded Lyceum Ballroom. "Moonlight Serenade" plays.

PHOEBE: *(to herself)* I feel like a traitor. Phoebe! Fancy coming here. The Lyceum! Saturday night! The hunting ground. Boys looking for girls! Girls pretending they're not looking for boys. Maisie! I feel like a *meshuggener*! So embarrassed standing here, without you. How can I dance when you are dead? I'm going home.

VOICE: Hey! Where you going in such a hurry?

PHOEBE: Home!

VOICE: No! Wait! I've been looking for you everywhere!

PHOEBE: That's an original chat-up line. Must go. Sorry! So-long.

VOICE: Wait! You can't run away from me now. Our meeting was ordained.

PHOEBE: You Yanks!

VOICE: I'm Paul. Lieutenant Paul Gottlieb from Baltimore. What's your name?

PHOEBE: Phoebe. Phoebe Myers.

PAUL: What a wonderful name. It fits. Phoebe Myers. Phoebe comes from the Greek. It means pure! Bright! Radiant!

186

PHOEBE: Clever dick. As if I didn't know.

PAUL: Sorry. I didn't mean to patronise you. Of course you would know. Phoebe! You are my anima.

PHOEBE: You're very polite and quite clever, for a Yank.

PAUL: Who's patronising whom? Phoebe! How wonderful to find you. I was passing. I heard the music. It's fate.

PHOEBE: *(she sighs)* Fate rules our lives.

PAUL: That was a real sigh. The Esperanto of the Jewish world.

PHOEBE: My best friend was killed this week.

PAUL: I'm sorry. What can I say?

PHOEBE: Paul Gottlieb from Baltimore. Say nothing. Nothing can heal this wound. Still, as my mother says. One door closes. Another door closes.

PAUL: I can see the sadness in your eyes. *(they dance, she laughs)*

PHOEBE: You read my utter desolation. I am a blatant pessimist.

PAUL: You're far too young to be cynical.

PHOEBE: I love dancing. Only dancing transports me.

PAUL: You are so very beautiful.

PHOEBE: Get your eyes tested, before we meet again.

PAUL: Oh? Does that means you want to see me again?

The band plays "Long Ago and Far Away", they are dancing. More dance music.

PHOEBE: Time flies?

PAUL: Where does it go?

PHOEBE: You sound like me. Home to the East End. Goodbye!

PAUL: Hey! What about us? Are we going to meet again?

PHOEBE: Maybe next Wednesday.

PAUL: I'll be here.

PHOEBE: Good. Goodnight.

END SCENE

NEW SCENE: Music "Zarathrustra" by Richard Strauss.

PHOEBE: *(entering, she calls)* I'm home!

FAY: Phoebe! Sweetheart! Enjoy yourself?

PHOEBE: Quite!

FAY: Meet someone nice?

PHOEBE: No. Hello dad!

FAY: He's lost, somewhere deep in Teutonic forests.

PHOEBE: Of all places for a little Jewish tailor!

JOE: Music's the only thing that makes life worthwhile. Oh? Hello darling? You home?

PHOEBE: No. I'm still at the Lyceum.

JOE: Phoebe! Listen! This is the loveliest music in the world! So how can people who make such beautiful music do such monstrous things?

PHOEBE: Going to bed. Goodnight! Oh mum! By the way, I met someone.

FAY: *(trying casual)* Oh? Was he nice?

PHOEBE: He seemed very nice. But who can tell?

FAY: Meeting him again?

PHOEBE: *(yawning)* Goodnight. *END SCENE.*

The music continues. PHOEBE enters her bedroom

PHOEBE: Hello horror!

SYLVIE: Was he a Yank? Hey babe! What a swell figure. Let's get horizontal. Did he kiss you?

PHOEBE: I bought myself a new diary today.

SYLVIE: Did it thrill you? Did he touch you? Please!

PHOEBE: I'll touch you. See this pillow? I'm going to knock you silly!

SYLVIE: That's not fair. *(PHOEBE whacks SYLVIE)* You're the worst sister in the world. Where did he touch you? Did he slowly stroke your pointy titties?

PHOEBE: You've got a mind like a sewer. Look at my new diary.

SYLVIE: Beautiful. Real *schmutter*! You've been writing. Let me see.

PHOEBE: Shut up and go to sleep.

SYLVIE: Love you. Night-night. What's his name?

PHOEBE: Paul!

SYLVIE: If he impressed you he must be special. Night-night!

PHOEBE: Goodnight Sylvie. Love you. *(PHOEBE starts writing, using her special inner diary voice)*

Dear Maisie! I bought this diary today. To talk to you! I'm under the blankets with a torch in my left hand.

It just struck me. You're stuck at eighteen and will never get older. I'll be sending you all my thoughts, all my secrets. All my dreams. We were such great pals! Sometimes I wish I could die and join you. But mostly I want to stay alive, to keep you alive. *(distant laugher)* I can hear you laughing. Even now.

Met a boy tonight. At the Lyceum. His name's Paul. A Yank. Different from the others. He's very gentle, and has such beautiful eye-lashes! Signing off now. Goodnight Maisie. I'll be in touch. *(she yawns)* Dead tired! Can hardly — Love you. Forever.

END SCENE

The Lyceum Ballroom, The Strand. The couple jive to "In The Mood".

PHOEBE: *(singing with the vocalist)* Mr Whatyoucallit, what you doing tonight? — I just love jive. I could jive all night.

PAUL: I could do with some fresh air.

PHOEBE: Okay! But promise to bring me back.

PAUL: Let's go for a walk.

PHOEBE: *(her inner voice)* Maisie! We went down to the river. My heart pounding. Something's happened to me. Like wires touching, sparking. Shooting like stars across the water.

PHOEBE: I long to see the lights of London again.

PAUL: Phoebe! I long to kiss you.

PHOEBE: Long on.

PAUL: Please!

PHOEBE: No!

PAUL: Why no?

PHOEBE: Please don't be like the others.

PAUL: Ah! There have been others!

PHOEBE: You must know the jokes. One Yank and they're down.

PAUL: You know nothing about me. May I tell you?

PHOEBE: If you like.

PAUL: I was studying medicine, until this. Now I'm a lieutenant in the Intelligence Corp. I speak five languages, well. My father is Vice Dean at Johns Hopkins University, in Baltimore. He's a scientist. My mother swims. And bakes apple cakes.

PHOEBE: I can smell them now. I'm an exalted and experienced dress machinist. Before the war my Mum worked in a cigar factory. My father is a bespoke tailor. Tell me more.

PAUL: One kiss tells more than a thousand words.

PHOEBE: Yanks!

PAUL: Please! The first time I've begged in my life.

PHOEBE: So! Kiss me! What you waiting for? *(they kiss)* Thank you!

PAUL: My pleasure.

PHOEBE: That was very nice. Paul! *(they kiss again)*

PAUL: I respect you. I respect you.

PHOEBE: Just shut up and kiss me. Can't waste time in war. *(the siren sounds)*

PHOEBE: Let's get back to the Lyceum!

Dance tunes tumble upon each other, denoting time passing at the Lyceum. Waltz! Foxtrot! Jitterbug! Hoakey Coakey! Then "Moonlight Serenade".

PAUL: I must see you tomorrow.

PHOEBE: Must is an urgent world.

PAUL: And every evening before I go!

PHOEBE: Is it soon? Please tell me.

PAUL: Not now. Just dance.

PHOEBE: Hold me tight. *END SCENE*

NEW SCENE. Days later PHOEBE is writing in her diary. JOE plays "The Valkeries" by Wagner.

PHOEBE: It's June 1944 Maisie. The invasion is expected any day now and I'm in love. It's painful; like someone pulling out my *kishkers*!

JOE: She's at it again Fay! Lost in that little book.

FAY: Her own world might be preferable to this one.

SYLVIE: *(chanting)* Phoebe's fallen in looove! Drowning in a sea of passion. It's so much better than our weekly sweet ration!

JOE: What time is your Yank coming? Phoebe?

PHOEBE: What? Oh! Anytime now.

JOE: She's known the boy two weeks and already he's been invited home. The world's gone mad.

SYLVIE: Can't wait to see him. Do I look nice?

FAY: Lovely! Everything's lovely. The soup is ready. The *matzo* balls are bubbling away to perfection. The *Shobbos chola* looks so beautiful on the table. Phoebe! He's a little late so I'm lighting the candles.

PHOEBE: If you must you must.

JOE: She's known him two weeks. So? Inviting him home is far too soon. I know he sounds like a nice, respectable boy, but usually they're only after one thing.

191

SYLVIE: What thing is that dad?

PHOEBE: Please! Everyone!

FAY: Beautiful! Candles light up a dark world.

SYLVIE: I'm starving. Can I eat?

FAY: Sylvie! It's Friday night. Our beautiful white tablecloth is spread before us. So shut up. *(the doorbell rings)* Ah! There he is. Now behave.

SYLVIE: Why should I?

PHOEBE: Oh god! This is going to be terrible.

JOE: I'll be quieter than the grave.

PHOEBE: Take a *schtum* powder everyone. *(she goes to the door and opens it)* Paul! Please come in.

PAUL: Candles! How beautiful! Sorry I'm late.

FAY: Welcome Paul to our Sabbath home.

PAUL: Thank you. How nice.

PHOEBE: Paul. This is Fay. My mother. My father Joe, and that's my kid sister Sylvie.

SYLVIE: I am not a kid. I am a human being!

JOE: Oh? Thanks for telling us.

PAUL: I'm delighted to meet you all.

FAY: Please! Sit! The *lokshen* soup is piping hot. So enjoy! Sabbath is the queen.

PAUL: How kind. And how marvellous! A white tablecloth!

SYLVIE: How polite he is!

JOE: So, you met my daughter at the Lyceum. Incidentally! Did she tell you her best friend Maisie was killed by a doodlebug, just over a week ago?

PAUL: No! How terrible.

PHOEBE: Welcome to the East End of London. Where everything is rationed, except talk.

PAUL: *(eating)* This is the best soup I ever had.

FAY: Chicken soup goes into the main artery and straight to the soul!

JOE: Incidentally Paul, what are your intentions towards my lovely daughter?

PHOEBE: Dad!

FAY: Joe!

PAUL: It's all right. Mr Myers. My intentions are as pure as the person my eyes are fixed upon. My Sabbath Queen. Phoebe!

SYLVIE: How sweet! How romantic!

JOE: What a nice boy! Isn't he nice? *(they laugh)*

FAY: Eat! Enjoy. And good *Shobbos* to all of us! *END SCENE*

Later. The Embankment. Al Bowley sings "Love is the Sweetest Thing".

PAUL: What are you thinking?

PHOEBE: Sorry. I was miles away. Remembering a song Maisie loved. This embankment is our tryst!

PAUL: An embankment holds back the torrent. Phoebe! I'm finding it hard to hold back the flood.

PHOEBE: Look! The full moon!

PAUL: We're destined for each other.

PHOEBE: Yes. In that case kiss me! *(they kiss)*

PAUL: I have news.

PHOEBE: News is never good. Don't tell me.

PAUL: I have no choice. We're leaving.

PHOEBE: When?

PAUL: Four days. June the 8th. In the early morning.

PHOEBE: *(trying to be casual)* Oh dear.

PAUL: I'll come back and we'll get engaged. I promise. If you want that! And then married.

PHOEBE: Will I hear from you?

PAUL: I'll write every, every day. If I am able. Be happy now.

PHOEBE: Something marvellous has happened to us.

PAUL: I love you and I am in love with you.

PHOEBE: Then there's nothing to fear. Paul. Take me somewhere.

PAUL: Somewhere? Oh! You absolutely sure?

PHOEBE: As sure as my heartbeat.

PAUL: This is your first time? Of course?

PHOEBE: Of course! What do you think?

PAUL: I think you are the most beautiful girl in the world.

PHOEBE: I want you to make love to me.

PAUL: Phoebe! Where shall we go?

PHOEBE: Certainly not here!

PAUL: I noticed a small hotel on the way here. In Villiers Street.

PHOEBE: Let's go. *END SCENE*

Al Bowley song "Love is the Sweetest Thing".

PHOEBE: Maisie! I'm in Whitechapel Reference Library, writing all this down. It was wonderful.

Hebrew love song "Dodi Li" from "The Song of Solomon".

PHOEBE: Maisie. Sexual passion is the most wonderful thing in the world. How tragic that you never experienced it. A man you love, inside you, is the zenith of life.

PHOEBE: *(now to PAUL)* I love you. I love you. I love you! Forever.

PAUL: Forever and ever! Let me breathe in the taste of you. The smell of you!

PHOEBE: "My beloved is mine and I am his. He feedeth among the lillies."

PHOEBE: After, we lay staring at the ceiling! Floating in timelessness. Then he asked me about you.

PAUL: Tell me about Maisie! Your friend.

PHOEBE: She's dead. It's over. Time the great healer, and all that crap. Then he took me back to Stepney.

PAUL: We will be together. For always!

PHOEBE: For always! Goodbye.

PAUL: Goodbye.

PHOEBE: And I watched him walk away. Maisie! That pain! In my stomach, in my head! That gnawing emptiness! *END SCENE.*

NEW SCENE. PHOEBE's home. JOE is working on his sewing machine.

JOE: I'm a genius. This suit is a poem. A symphony! Give a kick.

PHOEBE: What time is it?

FAY: Half past midnight. Darling! Stop pacing.

PHOEBE: What's the date today?

FAY: The fourteenth of July. As it was ten minutes ago. Phoebe. The lads are advancing deep into France. They'll soon be in Germany and the war will be over.

PHOEBE: Eight weeks! And not a word! He promised. I don't understand.

JOE: Who understands anything? Can I say something?

FAY: No!

JOE: It's possible he wasn't serious! He's a man! They're not nice like women. He meant well, but war embraces a different morality.

FAY: Joe! Shut up. I'm going to bed.

JOE: Me too. I shall accompany you upstairs my darling.

FAY: Phoebe! Please don't stay up too late. He'll be alright!

PHOEBE: *(she laughs sardonically)* Goodnight! *(her parents go)* Maisie! You're the only person I can talk to.

MAISIE: Best friends forever.

PHOEBE: Every day I wait for the postman. I watch him coming down the street. Now he just shakes his head. Maisie! I can't take not knowing. I can't get on with my life. I'm phoning the American Embassy in the morning. *END SCENE*

PHOEBE is in a phone box. Coins drop.

VOICE: American Embassy. Can I help you?

PHOEBE: Yes. My name is Phoebe Myers. I'm phoning about Paul Gottlieb. He's an officer in your Intelligence Corps. We were very close. He promised to write daily. He's been gone eight weeks and I haven't heard a word. He's from Baltimore. I just need to know if he's all right? Please!

VOICE: I'll put you through.

PHOEBE: Thank you! Maisie! I'm in a daze. A maze. Of days.

MAISIE: You should have been a poet.

VOICE 2: Hello? Miss Myers! Can I help you?

PHOEBE: Yes. He's Lieutenant Paul Gottlieb. From Baltimore. I just want to know if he's alive. We planned to get married.

VOICE 2: I see.

PHOEBE: We were in love.

VOICE 2: Sadly we cannot divulge classified information. But call back in a week's time. We may be able to provide some information.

PHOEBE: Thank you. His name Paul Gottlieb! From Baltimore! I'm Phoebe Myers. From Stepney!

VOICE 2: Thank you! Good morning.

PHOEBE: Maisie! I counted every minute. It was the longest week of my life. I couldn't go to work. I was sick, furious. Confused. I was trapped in a dark corner of myself. I hated him so much. I loved him so much. And then, somehow a week passed. *(coins drop into phone)*

I'm Phoebe Myers. I phoned last week. I just would prefer to know if Lieutenant Gottlieb is... dead.

VOICE 2: Ah yes. We do have a few details regarding Lieutenant Gottlieb.

PHOEBE: How kind of you.

VOICE 2: All we are able to divulge is that Lieutenant Gottlieb is not dead, and he is on active duty somewhere in Europe.

PHOEBE: Thank you. Goodbye! *FADE. (she is now home)* Mum! He's alive. Someway I wish he was dead. The pain's too much to bear.

FAY: Phoebe! I also carry pain.

PHOEBE: Please! Mother! Don't tell me about your problems.

FAY: You must go out. Meet people. Make new friends.

PHOEBE: The days of friendship are over. I'm not leaving this room.

FAY: Yes you are! We're going out. There's something I must tell you. So, up you get. Come on! *SCENE ENDS*

NEW SCENE. A little park. Birds sing. A busker plays on mouth organ "You Are My Sunshine".

PHOEBE: Itchy Park! Why did you bring me here? Only tramps come here.

FAY: It's nice and breezy. A little bit of oxygen in the middle of the choke! Let's sit here.

PHOEBE: Only down and outs hang about here.

FAY: Yeah! From the Salvation Army down the road. Have *rachmunis*!

PHOEBE: Compassion? You and your *stetyl* talk. Mum, we're in England. You were born here. We speak English in this country! Remember?

FAY: Sit down. Take your weight off your brain. Yes! We fought for these streets!

PHOEBE: Mum! You dragged me out to tell me something.

FAY: Yes. I also had a life. October the fourth! 1936. Only eight years ago. The Battle of Cable Street.

PHOEBE: Oh not that again!

FAY: *(ignoring her daughter)* Mosley tried to march through our Jewish heartland. Six thousand police to protect him. And

197

those *momser* police on horses charging. Us! Bastards. I can hear it all now!

Crowds. Horses! Shouting! Cheering! Booing!

VOICES: The Yids! The Yids! We've got to get rid of the Yids!

VOICES: They shall not pass! Mosley shall not pass!

FAY: And they didn't. We won the day! It was marvellous.

PHOEBE: Mum! You brought me here to tell me this?

FAY: Listen! Not a soul must know what I'm telling you. Especially your dad!

PHOEBE: Can we walk?

FAY: Why not? That battle changed my life. I became political.

PHOEBE: You? *(they are walking)* My mum? Political?

FAY: I kept it quiet from you. Joe always ridiculed me. You? A radical? I loved it. I joined the Young Communist League. Sold *Daily Workers* outside Whitechapel Station. Went to meetings. Demonstrations! I wanted to change the world. All by myself. But soon it dawned on me that all the women were being treated as inferior beings. The same old story. The men make the speeches and the women make the tea. So I left the comrades and one day, by chance I found myself right here.

PHOEBE: Alie Street! What happened here?

FAY: There was a group in that very building, the Workers Circle. Anarchists. Pacifists. Liberals. Disillusioned communists. A proper mishmash! I can hear it all now! Nothing really dies. The hymn of the Socialist movement! The "Internationale"!

Far off, a rousing version of the "Internationale".

FAY: The Anarchists! Suddenly I felt connected. And here I met David. He attracted me beyond all reason. I lost all restraint. He was gorgeous! His thick black hair! Beautiful nose. His fire! His piercing eyes. Like a biblical prophet. You can guess what happened. He took me to his little room in Assembly Passage — and possessed me. Day after day we made mad love. Incessant love. Incessant joy. You were about ten years old at that time. Now you know. No-one else suspected. Remember! Not a dickey bird to anyone. Do you forgive me?

PHOEBE: Mum! Of course! Anyway, forgiving is God's job.

FAY: Your father never found out. And he mustn't! Ever! Phoebe! In his little attic in Assembly Passage David transported me to places I never knew existed. He injected me with fire. Your dad never even noticed the love bites on my thighs. David consumed me for three years. And then — and then — he died. A stroke! Suddenly! In the reading room! Whitechapel Library. Let's go! Phoebe I get on with my life. *(they continue walking)* And so must you.

PHOEBE: Mum! You've been through the same fire that's consuming me.

FAY: Of course! *(they hug)* Phoebe! We bury the dead and get on with our lives. And things gradually get better. Here we are. Home. I wasn't aware we were that close. Not a single word to a single soul. Promise?

PHOEBE: I'm as silent as the grave.

FAY: Never tell a friend a secret, because your friend has a friend.

PHOEBE: Friends are in short supply these days. *FADE*

NEW SCENE. Years have passed. A wedding celebration is taking place in a hall. People are enjoying themselves. A small band plays "Chosen Chale Mazeltov".

PHOEBE: Maisie! It's nineteen sixty. Sylvie's got married today. Can you believe it? All those years gobbled up. For you it's a speck in endlessness. Time is even more mysterious than God. We haven't talked for a long time. I feel guilty. Forgive me but I've been so busy. I haven't opened my diary for yonks.

SYLVIE: Phoebe — still talking to yourself?

PHOEBE: Sylvie! You are such an exquisite bride. *("Always" plays)* I am so very happy for you.

SYLVIE:Then please show it.

PHOEBE: I'll do cartwheels in five minutes.

SYLVIE: *(she laughs and goes)* Toodlepip!

PHOEBE: Maisie! Did I tell you that I'm also married?

MAISIE: So, you left me in the dark? So? I'm only your best friend. So, who is he?

PHOEBE: Maurice! A nice, decent man! A chartered surveyor.

MAISIE: Nice! A good living.

PHOEBE: More like a dying.

MAISIE: So why weren't you in touch?

PHOEBE: I closed the diary because there was nothing to tell.

MAISIE: So, with all your principles you compromised.

PHOEBE: What's wrong with compromise? I've been married for almost eight years now.

MAISIE: What about you know who?

PHOEBE: Love dies Maisie! Time heals all wounds. Maurice is very nice. Easy going.

MAISIE: Paul never wrote then?

PHOEBE: I have two wonderful boys.

MAISIE: *Mazeltov*!

BOY: Mum! I'm bored. Come! Get me some more cake.

SECOND BOY: And me.

PHOEBE: Coming soon. Two lovely boys. Handsome like the wind! Aaron and Ben. And there's Maurice. Waving across the wilderness of the tribe. I could have done far worse.

FAY: Phoebe! There you are! Where you been hiding?

PHOEBE: Mum! You look pale. Anything wrong?

FAY: What could be wrong?

JOE: Nothing! Nothing. I've never seen her so happy.

FAY: I shouldn't be happy on such a day? My youngest daughter married!

JOE: Yes! Life for all its vagaries, is wonderful.

FAY: Phoebe! Isn't this a glorious day?

PHOEBE: It's perfect. I am so happy for Sylvie.

FAY: Good. Then dance with your dad.

PHOEBE: I will. Come on Dad! *(FAY goes. PHOEBE dances with JOE)* Ten years Maisie. Ten years flashed past. In this wasteland of nothingness.

JOE: Don't move your lips so much darling, or they'll call an ambulance.

PHOEBE: Ten years of my life, gone! Ten cold, chilling years. I'm coming. Must go dad! I promised to get the boys more cake. So long Maisie! See you soon.

MAISIE: Have fun!

PHOEBE: I must get on with my life. My lovely boys! That's all I need. Closing you down now Maisie! *END SCENE*

More time passes "Time Waits for No-one".

PHOEBE: Maisie! It's 1963. And I'm forty-one years old today. Five birthday cards. And one from — you'll never guess. It had an American stamp on the envelope. It was from Baltimore. I wanted to chuck it away but I shoved it down my bra. Later I went to the reading room. Whitechapel Library. My hands shook when I opened it.

PAUL: "Dear Phoebe! I know this will be like a bolt out the blue. For nineteen years I've carried this enormous burden of guilt. Maybe you can forgive me when I explain what happened. At first the madness of war gave me no time to write. Around February 1945 I was ordered to Ravensbruck Concentration Camp, near Berlin. It was hell. I saw a young girl propped against a wall. She was barely breathing. Her name was Hilda. I felt it my duty to try and bring her back to life. One felt obligated to her and one thing led to another. Try and understand. You are such a compassionate person. I felt I owed her some life. I took her back to Baltimore and married her. *(his voice starts to fade)* Phoebe! It didn't turn out well and I never stopped loving you. How I've longed for you all these years and those idyllic days in London! I am crying. Please forgive me —" Etcetera! Etcetera! And so on. *(she yawns)*

Phoebe: Maisie! I couldn't allow him to destroy me twice. I tore the letter into tiny fragments. *END SCENE*

NEW SCENE

Phoebe: Another eight years down the plug-hole, Maisie. My little babies are such big boys; almost men. And I'm almost fifty. And my mother is dying, Maisie!

Fay: Phoebe! Please put on a lovely tune...

"Rozhinkes mit Mandlen" plays.

Fay: *Rozhinkes mit Mandlen*! Almonds and Raisins. The bitter and the sweet. Life!

Phoebe: How are you, darling?

Fay: I'm fine. I'm going through the door that leads nowhere. Celebrate my life, darling. Celebrate life itself. Life is a celebration against the dark. Against all the odds.

Phoebe: Then she breathed in, but she never breathed out.

A Rabbi intones the prayers for the dead. Others join in.

Phoebe: And now she is in the ground. Plashet Grove Cemetery. Near Ilford! She's joined you Maisie. In the great nothingness. Near Ilford. Mum's dead and my marriage is dying. And Paul's dead to me. *(telephone rings)* Oh yes! Something else happened. Yesterday! As a matter of fact. Guess who broke into my quiet, polished life?

The telephone rings

Paul: Phoebe!

Phoebe: Who's that?

Paul: A voice from the blue. Phoebe! It's Paul. I'm in London. On business. The Cumberland Hotel! Marble Arch! I must see you. Please Phoebe. I understand how you feel. I'm only here overnight. Phoebe! You are the only woman I ever loved. *(PHOEBE laughs heartily)*

Maisie: So, what did you do?

Phoebe: I got a taxi all the way to the West End. When I got to the Cumberland I went straight upstairs. I knocked on the door. He opened it.

Maisie: What happened then?

Phoebe: I took off my clothes and got into bed.

Maisie: No? Oh my god!

Phoebe: Paul! Love me! Obliterate everything. And he did. In the dark our bodies fused. Melted. It was perfect.

Paul: At last. Together at last.

Phoebe: For a moment time stopped! But then he put on the light and got out of bed. I couldn't stop myself laughing. Paul was a balding, fat, middle-aged, pot-bellied businessman, from Baltimore! My Paul died in 1944. A stranger inhabited his body.

Paul: What are you doing?

Phoebe: Getting dressed.

Paul: I don't understand! Please stay with me!

Phoebe: Paul. I'm putting on my overcoat and I'm leaving. Don't be in touch.

Paul: Phoebe! I'm getting a divorce. I've cleared the way for us. Hilda knows. She understands. Where are you going?

Phoebe: Home. Back to reality!

Paul: Phoebe! You must stay with me.

Phoebe: I stayed too long. Goodbye, whoever you are. And Maisie. I closed the door and caught a number twenty-five bus to Stepney. To see how my father was surviving. Maisie! You can now stay dead.

Maisie: Wait! Phoebe! Keep in touch. You need me.

Phoebe: Life is sweet Maisie! As for me, I look forward to my grandchildren! My immortality. So long!

Grieg's "Wedding Day at Troldhaugen" plays

Phoebe: Hello Dad! That's much better than your Nazi *momser*! Mum would be pleased. How are you darling?

Joe: No better. No worse.

Phoebe: That's an improvement. Just popped in to see if you were managing.

JOE: Who manages?

PHOEBE: Why do you answer a question with a question?

JOE: Do I? *(they both laugh)*

PHOEBE: I'm going home now.

JOE: Where else? Anyway I need an early night. Got to dash. Saville Row in the morning.

PHOEBE: The suit's beautiful. You're an artist.

JOE: You bet! Goodnight sweetheart. You look radiant tonight.

PHOEBE: Thanks Dad! Do you remember Maisie?

JOE: Maisie? Course I do! Why drag her up?

PHOEBE: She just came to mind. Maurice will be wondering where I am. Goodnight! Don't let your memories bite. *(she opens the door)* Look! A full moon. Not too far to go. Think I'll walk home. "How many miles to Babylon. Three score and ten. Will we get there by candlelight? Yes! And back again."

She walks. "Moonlight Serenade" plays.

---

from **Yes from No Man's Land**

"Someone walked over my grave." The old man shuddered as he talked to himself.

The nun came to the bed yet again and this time she stuck a needle into his arm.

"You're taking my blood again. My blood again." Then he cursed her in Yiddish.

"*Momsers! Gunofs!*"

She smiled. She had lost count of the times she had told him that she wasn't taking blood. "This will help you rest," she said.

"Nuns for nurses. Whoever heard of such a thing?" He questioned the air and then he blew seven times through his fingers at her receding face.

He closed his eyes and spoke to himself again, but he could not be sure if he was speaking the words aloud.

"The one thing I don't understand — why a Catholic Hospital? Wasn't I a good father? Why did my children bring me to this?"

> *Then in the darkness he saw Manny again. His son Manny.*
> *"What are you doing there? You Jews in England! What are you doing in the rain and the cold?" The deep voice of Manny boomed across the ward. "What are you doing going nowhere? You Jews in England!"*

Then Joe Levene remembered that this son, his oldest, was in Israel and these words were spoken the last time he came to London, three years before; before he went back and lost touch forever.

He wanted to banish the image of his son.

"Leave me alone Manny, you're driving me mad." But still the voice persisted.

"What are you doing there, dying in the dark?"

"Dying? Who's dying?" The old man edged himself up, but by the time he was sitting the voice and the face of his lost son faded.

"He can talk. Made a real mess of his life. Calls it idealism."

From *Yes from No Man's Land,* a novel (1965)

But the man in the next bed wasn't interested. Joe screwed up his eyes as he gazed right across the bright ward. Then he sunk back down into his bed and thought of his other children.

"Wasn't I always a good father? Why did you drag me down to this Jesus place? Didn't I always do my duty?"

Sophie nodded agreement but Barry laughed.

Then Joe saw Sarah again. His dead wife. She came and went all the time now. He remembered how he used to feel her in the middle of the night, when she was sleeping. How he used to wake up in the middle of the night; sometimes afraid. But all that was a long time ago. Once he cried his tears down her warm body.

"Go back to sleep Joe." She said, stirring and moaning.

"I had to believe in God. I had to give God to my kids." He had to explain to her again and again.

"I didn't even know how to behave like a son to my own father but was suddenly expected to behave like a father to my own children. But I succeeded. You have to admit. I gave them a sense of purpose. Didn't I?"

There was no reply. He knew she was dead. He knew his mind was wandering.

Joe groped for the top of the locker for he was sure that there was a glass of lemon tea somewhere, but all his hand found was a tumbler of water. He thirstily drained it down, and then with surprising speed he jumped out of bed.

"Nurse! Nurse! He's out of his bed again. Nurse! Nurse!"

The old nun with the Irish accent rushed towards the glass door just as he reached it, then gently chiding, she led him back to his bed.

"The doctor said I needed exercise. He said I'd be as right as rain with exercise." He climbed back between the sheets, pushing away her helping hands.

She primped the pillow behind his head and his wild eyes darted in every direction, at the men in the other beds, fixing each face with a look of disgust. "*Goyim!* What can you expect?" He would have cursed them more substantially but he remembered that they were ill, and he wasn't taking any chances.

The nun wiped his mouth and combed his hair and while he muttered she cooed to him as if he were a baby.

"There, there. Dearie me. Dear, dear, you naughty little boy."

"I want to go home," he said.

"It's almost visiting time Poppa, so be a good boy."

He closed his eyes so as not to see her, so as not to see the cross dangling from her neck. "A nun. Ain't never had none." He laughed.

And there in the darkness of his closed eyes he swayed backwards and forward, hoping that the face of his dead wife would come back again, or the voice of his youngest son or his father, or his mother.

It was almost visiting time; relatives were quietly waiting outside the ward; all of them trying to appear casual and unconcerned. A child cuddled her doll as she scolded it. Her voice was the only sound apart from the fast footsteps of the nurses along the corridors. People crowded through the main entrance holding flowers and fruit; people unaccustomed to buying flowers except for births, marriages and deaths. These flowers were for death. This was a 'Hostel of God'.

Once the building had been a gaunt Victorian monstrosity and was called the Hackney Hospital for the Dying. But just after the war they tore the guts out, gave it a face-lift and changed its name; and even though the function of the place was exactly the same, at least the patients did not know that they were to die.

Outside it was Sunday. The wet narrow streets were bathed in the sickening orange light of street lamps. The whole area smelled of peardrops or soap, or possibly it was the smell of the gasworks.

But the 'Hostel of God' stood a little back from the main road. There were trees in the grounds and bushes and flowers and there was a rather modern statue of Jesus Christ. He was turned away from the street, his arms wide open, embracing the whole hospital.

The doctor passed along the ward with a sister, stopping a little while at every bed, trying to finish his round before the visitors were allowed in. He was very surprised to find Joe Levene silent. It was usually most difficult getting away from his bed. The doctor looked at the chart and nodded as the nun softly spoke.

"How are we today Mr Levene?" The doctor went closer to the man. "I said — I wondered how you were Mr Levene?"

The old man looked at him but did not reply.

The doctor was sure that this patient did not know he was

going to die. At least, not on the surface. Like the other patients he probably knew deep down, but he would never admit it to himself, never let it come to the point of words, even if it did manage to come to the brink of the mind. For to speak about the disease only gave it reality, only brought the vaguely possible into the almost probable. Words gave the disease a form of benediction.

The doctor was pretty sure that this patient would not have too bad a death. He was old enough to ease himself, through coma and sleep, into the hereafter. The young suffered the most. Young bodies tended to fight back at cancer; they did not go with the disease; they would not lay down and let it flow over them and conquer them. Fighting the disease brought the agony.

No, they would not have too bad a time with Mr Levene. They were lucky in this hospital, taking all in all, considering the nature of the disease from which they were dying. Perhaps it was because more than three-quarters of the patients were old. People did not die too noisily in Hackney; perhaps they were too embarrassed at making too much fuss. In Hackney they seemed to die with the minimum amount of emotion; the way they lived.

But the faraway face of the old Jew saddened the doctor. He wondered why. For so many faces filled these beds. They came and went sooner than the seasons. So many had come and gone since he had been there. One got used to it.

Yet every so often a certain face got stuck in the memory.

The old Jew had such a face.

"What's the score doctor? How am I doing?" The face suddenly quickened.

"Coming along nicely." The doctor replied. He felt tired; he didn't know why he should feel sad for the old man. He would not suffer anywhere near as bad as the young man near the door, who even now was stretched within that most terrible last agony.

"I want to go home."

"Be patient Mr Levene. All in good time." The doctor was glad that he would be off duty in half an hour. He went through the brisk examination mechanically, listening to the old man, and answering him.

"So when am I being discharged?" The old man sat up completely, to show how well he was and he offered the doctor a sweet.

"Thanks. It won't be long now." He muttered and smiled, popped the sweet under his tongue and moved to the next bed.

Soon he would be at the young man's bed. And the young man would be groaning as his body cracked and splintered, and the pain rose out of the guts and screamed down his bones. In the end he would die of the drugs and not of the pain. And he would be glad to die. He didn't relish standing over the fearful eyes of the young man. For the eyes would say "How is it that you are healthy? That you will live and I must die? And die like this."

The young man knew he had cancer. Maybe that's why he feared him. The old Jew didn't know, not consciously, maybe that's why he was sad for him. But no. Most of them didn't know. It was something else. It was strange how most faces faded away, faces of men who came and went, endlessly. And one face, occasionally, got stuck in the memory.

The doctor went to the next bed and the next bed, getting ever closer to the fearful eyes of the young man, dying near the door.

Joe could see the face of his dead wife again. All the suffering had gone now; all the suffering of the later years had gone from her face. His fingers groped forward but they poked right through her. He didn't mind her not smiling, she had not smiled much in her life. She was not like any other woman in the East End and always seemed out of place there. She was not one to get over-excited. Sarah was a listener.

"Yes, you understood people because you listened to them. You could see right through them."

She screwed up her face as if in pain; he could never understand why she hated words of praise.

"You're a practical woman Sarah, a beautiful practical woman. I loved you with all heart and soul. I still love you."

She started to walk away from him. "I've got other things to think about." She said, waving him away.

He knew why she was angry. "All right. So I'm sorry. So I married again. Terrible thing. I was lonely."

The face faded. Her white hair blew away, like smoke.

Joe searched for his tobacco pouch; he fumbled in the bedclothes and then remembered it was in his locker. He lit the pipe and sucked the sweet smoke contentedly; he had always enjoyed a good smoke. It was one of his few pleasures, so he always said, but he said this about all his pleasures, like reading, eating toffees, listening to the radio, having a good chinwag, eating a nice piece of fried fish, watching his grandchildren, listening to good music, etcetera, etcetera, etcetera.

He opened his eyes with a start, realised he had almost dozed off again and that the pipe had dropped from his lips. He smelled burning and excitedly brushed the hot ash from the bed cover.

"It's nothing. Nothing."

How many times had Sarah warned him? For years, for donkey's years. He had lost count.

"You'll catch yourself alight." She had said it over and over again. Sometimes he woke in the middle of the night with the pipe barely hanging from his slightly open lips. "You'll catch yourself alight." She said it yet again.

"I ain't died in my bed, yet."

The man in the next bed looked over the top of his newspaper. The old Jew was talking to himself again; he didn't dislike the old Jew, not really. Sometimes the old Jew gave him a piece of honey cake. He loved honey cake. And sometimes some sugared almonds. The thin face went down again behind the middle pages of the Sunday newspaper.

Joe saw the face again. Or was it Manny this time? Was it his face? He tried to concentrate. "Don't do me no favours. Manny's face I can do without."

He knew it was the drugs that made the faces come. The doctor explained that sometimes it happened that way. But it would all be over in a few weeks. The doctor promised. "Mr Levene, you'll be as right as rain." He said. But Manny's voice had a way of persisting; nothing could shut it out.

"I do not wave the flag. I do not feel any political or religious attachment for the earth of Israel. It's just that this place has grown on me. It's the place that least offends me."

Joe sighed; he had never managed to go up to Jerusalem; had never been totally sure it was worth going up to. Anyway he had never found the opportunity or the drive or the time. He remembered chiding Manny for not bringing his grandchildren over the last time he came, the last time before he lost contact forever.

"You see Manny, children leave you. But when they marry they have kids and they come back to you. Grandchildren make you less lonely. They give new life to the family." But Joe could see that Manny wasn't listening, he was going on about something else. "One day my son came home from the American

Embassy; he was playing there with an official's child. And for the first time he said — '*Abba*, what's a Jew?'"

"I asked him why he wanted to know and he replied that his friend said he didn't like Jews and my son Aaron told him that he didn't like Jews either. 'But what are Jews *Abba*?' And this, dear father of mine, is precisely the reason why I stay in Israel. For even if our backs are still against the wall, at least, at last, they are against our own wall."

"Manny, do me a favour. Stay in Israel. Vanish, fade. I want to speak to your mother."

Again he thought of the menorah. *He knew that he would never forget it until the day he died. He closed his eyes, clenched them tight and tried to see it again. He forced his mind away from the Jesus coughing place, and through the darkness and across the sea; across the flat dark earth of Europe. He strove to see the long table in the only lighted room in Poland.*

Yes! He could just now see the shape of his mother, all smoky as she dovened *backwards and forwards in front of the light, passing her hands in prayer over the flames, over the whole of Warsaw; but he could not see the candlestick. He could not see her face or the candles burning. It was useless, the room was receding; he could not hold on to it. It was gone.*

No, it would never go out of his mind, that candlestick.

"It has been in the family a long time. Take care of it." His father said.

And he wondered now why they should have given him such a present, such an honour. So he brought the silver menorah *across the whole of Europe, afraid even to put it into his case, clutching it under his vest, against his flesh, all the way from Warsaw to the Mouth of London. And Sarah was there again, sleeping, turned to the wall.*

"You know why I'm angry." He said, pushing her. "You know why." And she finally woke up, turned over, looked at him and shook her head.

"I said pawn anything. Everything. But not the candlestick. Never that candlestick. It must never leave the family. And you promised. Remember?"

"You can't eat candlesticks." She replied.

"It was handed down. I brought it from Warsaw. It was our faith." He raised his voice, then remembering he was in Hackney, talking to himself, he stroked her face, her cool face. "It was our faith, our faith." He almost sang as he stroked her hair.

"I'd even pawn my faith to feed my kids."

Then she turned over to the wall and was gone.

211

Joe Levene sat up, put the earphones on and conducted the music of Delius with the bowl of his pipe clutched in the palm of his hand.

Now he could see the visitors coming down the ward. She was not there. Sophie was late again. His eyesight was none too good but he was sure. You couldn't miss Sophie. A bus coming down the ward you could miss sooner than Sophie. Mind you she wasn't as fat as all that.

"After all, I'm not a prisoner! I ain't committed any crimes." He appealed to the nonplussed patient in the next bed.

"Are you feeling comfy Pop?" The nun stood over him again, pushed a flannel across his resisting face and fluffed his remaining hair into a high quiff.

He wished she would wipe the smile off her face. Something must be wrong with her life if she smiled all the time. He decided to just let her get on with it. He was at the mercy of Christians. "This is what my children have brought me to. I'm trapped. Cornered."

He didn't want their medicine or their poison gas. He didn't want their kindness, their help, their bullet in the brain in the middle of the night. Who were they trying to kid? The Jews were alone in the world. They couldn't count on no-one but themselves. "We don't want your kindness or your horror. Your pills or your poison gas. Neither your honey nor your sting." His voice rose to a crescendo and then, pitifully, he added. "I'm alone. All alone."

"She won't be long Poppa. You've got lovely children."

"Mind your own bloody business. What do you know of my kids? I've got the best kids in the world."

He never smiled at her. Never. And he hated to look at their faces. They all wore that same Jesus smile and they made him shudder. He remembered even as a child how he used to cross the streets in Warsaw if ever he saw nuns coming towards him. And he remembered those terrible statues of the Jesus figure, in his agony; all in that dead white marble. Jesus the turncoat. Jesus the Jew who started the death of Jews.

And the churches made him feel sick; they seemed so high when he was a child, so on top of him, as if they would crumble down and crush and bury him. And this agony man was their saviour.

He remembered once trying to find work, and all the tailors of

212

London was standing in the Mile End Road, unemployed, waiting, scheming. When out of the blue a Yiddisher feller sorted him out and tried to convert him to the *Yok* faith, no less.

"Believe in me and ye shall be saved." The little Yid said, in Yiddish. "Whoever heard of such a thing?"

And he remembered clearing his throat and spitting in the man's face, and it spoiled his day for the whole week.

And he raised his hand again and once more he spat without spit through his fingers at the close beaming face of the nun. "Nuns for nurses!"

Yet he had to admit to himself that they were kind. He didn't want to show it but he had to admit; not to them, not to his children but only to himself. Even if they did smell of cloves and mothballs and smiled all the time they weren't too bad. "But I can't afford the price I have to pay, in the middle of the night, when you try to suck the blood from my soul." But his voice had lost the sound of passion and was mere automatic meanderings as he watched her coming down the ward.

"You hear me nun? Not your pills nor your poison gas."

"Yes Poppa I heard you. There's a lovely little man." The nun was amused by the old Jew. She had lost count of the times he had said these things since he had been admitted. She found it odd that he should go on all the time about the Christians but she liked him and she liked his family; they were so close. That was the wonderful thing about the Jewish people; they believed in the family. She often waited with him until his daughter came; and she was always amused by the way that he thought he was so different from the other poor souls in the ward. However, she was concerned with the way that he denigrated the Lord, and she prayed for him. As she stood by the bed of the old man she gazed around the ward. Mr Levene always stressed his Jewishness, his aloneness. Yet how different was he? They even all looked the same, these dying men. Even though they came from all walks of life, from all classes, from all religions, here they were related. Here the thin threads were being pulled in by the hand of God and were being woven into a garment of common suffering. Pulled in by the hand of the Lord, for his own divine purpose.

She crossed herself not too noticeably.

"I hope she brings my clothes. I don't want no argument, only my clothes. I want to go home," Joe said.

"You'll be going home soon, so be a good boy. We're all going home." She could not resist this comforting aside.

"Leave me alone, just leave me alone. You've taken your blood for today."

"Very well. But promise you won't jump out of bed again."

He half smiled, like a furtive guilty child. "Go. Go — *gay gay*. I promise I won't do it again. Today."

The nun giggled and went to the next bed.

There she stopped smiling and for a moment she touched the warm hand of the quiet man. He looked up from his newspaper without any change in his expression. What a contrast there was between this poor thing and the old Jew. No one ever visited this patient. The nun could not remember ever seeing one person coming to visit Mr Hamilton. He never asked for anything, hardly said a word, never gave any trouble; some were like that, they came and they went and no one would have known that they had ever been there. Mr Hamilton believed in God. That helped.

Joe was disgusted with his daughter. "Manny is not exactly the apple of my eye, but he's a madman. I can't find any excuses for the others not coming. Even Barry could have gone out of his way for once in his life, as busy as he is. But for Sophie there's no excuse. I wash my hands. And even if she comes every day is that any reason for being late? Haven't I been a good father? Don't I deserve respect? Is that too much to ask?"

Again the sad white face of his dead wife floated before him. He wanted her to smile, all his life he wanted her to smile; change the expression on her face. The music in his ears was not so nice now, the sweet sound of Delius was gone. Tales of the Vienna Woods was playing.

"Muck. Vienna. City of my nightmare. Danube — so red, with blood. Place of Hitler. Come on Sarah, smile, smile." Just for a fraction of a second her moist eyes lit up and he believed she smiled at him.

Sarah had been dead for seven years. He knew the exact date. August 5th, 1957. Five minutes past eleven in the morning. She was the first girl he had ever taken out. She came from a better family, a well-to-do family. "How you agreed to me I don't know."

That made her crack her face. She nodded.

Her parents came from Odessa and went straight to Stamford Hill; they didn't even use the East End as a stepping stone.

"Sarah I want you to forgive me for marrying again."

She nodded again. Something was up. Today she was nodding and agreeing to everything too easily.

"I was lonely. I had to. Tell me you understand."

The face nodded, gently.

"How can you understand just like that?" He knew she was doing it merely for his benefit. He took off the earphones. She didn't understand.

But there was something else, something apart from the marrying again, something else he wanted to be forgiven for, but he dare not put it into words. But she knew. Sarah knew everything.

Between the death and the remarriage there had been the dark time. She knew. She witched him; she had floated in the room above him, above the bed. If you lived with someone for forty-two years they watched you when they were dead. They never left you. Yes, she saw him for five minutes or so, once a week or sometimes even twice, depending on how lonely he felt.

"I was lonely when you died. Went up West. You know that. The streets were full of lonely people. Believe me, there's nothing except a happy marriage. What else is there in the world?"

She shrugged.

"The streets were full of lonely old men. All their wives were dead, one way or another. I needed comfort, as you know. Listen, don't go. A woman grows up but a man carries the hunger, the pain of sex with him to his box. But you shouldn't have pawned the candlestick."

He looked around again for his daughter. It was unbelievable that she could be so late again.

"Life is sweet Sarah. The longer you live the more you realise — the more you want to hold on to it."

He was very tired now. He could see the visitors bustling around the other beds and everywhere was surrounded by flowers. The *Goyim* always brought flowers, never something nice to eat like a smoked salmon roll or a Dutch pound cake. He had no time for them.

The figure of his wife floated upwards and backwards, back into its usual lying position in the corner of the ceiling where he couldn't see it anymore. It was also tired, he supposed. He was calling her to come down too often. He wanted to lay down beside her.

"All my life I own nothing and now at last I am a man of property. I bought the bit of earth beside you. The burial society charged enough, but it was worth it."

Again he was burying her. His earth fell upon the wood and he wanted to jump into the hole. His children held him back. He cried. But at least she lay at Forest Gate where the air was sweeter and the birds found time to sing. At least she was nowhere near Mare Street and the gasworks and the stinking slums and the filth and the poverty.

"What are you doing? You Jews of England? What are you doing dying in the dark?" Manny, his firstborn was at it again.

He remembered the exact date. August 5th, five past eleven, 1957. That was when she had departed the world by way of the General Hospital, just near the Hackney Road.

"Who's dying? Leave me alone Manny. No, no, don't go."

But the sound of his son was gone.

"I'm all alone. Deserted by my children — my lovely wife dead. The Jews are all alone. I want to go home. All alone. Want to go home."

The faces of the Jesus girls came to taunt him. They all had the same face; smoke coming out of the hole in the mouth. Those Jesus girls. They tried to drag him down, they pulled him down to the dark dirty bed, took his money, his blood, his strength. Gave him only shame and despair and disgust in return.

"I'm glad you are what you are. You deserve to be prostitutes. No. Forgive me. I feel only sorrow for you. I weep for the loss, for the loss of innocence."

He knew that his eyes were wet but now he couldn't keep them open, no matter how he tried. The faces of the girls merged into one and then they faded. His head lolled forward and he was fast asleep.

* * *

Sophie Moss hurried down the ward with a mask-like grin on her rather fat face. She was out of breath and was relieved to see that her father was asleep.

She sat down and quickly held her side as a pain shot round from her spine to her ribs. It was the usual heartburn or something like that. She unwrapped a digestion tablet and popped it in her mouth.

He stirred and mumbled and she dabbed a handkerchief across her forehead.

"Dad! Dad! How are you Dad?" She called quietly, just in case he really was awake and was testing her again. But this time he really seemed asleep. She took off her coat and slumped back again into the chair, and sighed.

Her whole life was rush. How many times had she promised herself to slow down? She had lost count. There was never time to stand back or sit down and just do nothing. If only she could win some money and go away with Sam, just for a few weeks. Get the kids looked after.

She rubbed her side and breathed deeply. The pain was still there. Then she looked at her watch and listened to it. Then she thought of Sam and hoped that he had got the children off to bed all right and didn't let them get overexcited. Natalie had to go to the dentist ten-thirty the next morning.

"Forgive me," the old man suddenly said.

"What for?" Concerned, she held his hand, then noisily pulled her chair closer. "What for?

"I can't tell you what for. Just forgive me." He still hadn't opened his eyes.

"Of course I forgive you."

But then she realised he had been talking in his sleep. She blew her nose to get rid of the tears. There never seemed to be an end to tears. He seemed calm so she sat back.

Sophie glanced around the ward and watched the way the visitors were putting on their jolly show again.

Outside the ward, coming through the gates and in the corridors, these relatives were different people. Like sleepwalkers, stunned and silent. They only lit up when they entered the ward. Their frightening mechanical smiles reminded Sophie of the Punch and Judy puppets she once saw in Finsbury Park. In this ward they were all united. The dying and their relatives. For all those who watched their loved ones die were surely related. That was one lesson the dying could teach the living. Suffering knew no frontier, no class barrier. Death had no racial bar, death was no anti-semite. Death was not an exclusive gentile-only golf club. Her father could die here as good as anyone. An old Jew was not unduly out of place in such a desegregated place of suffering.

217

At first she couldn't believe he had such a terrible complaint (she hated saying it; that word — cancer). At first she believed that the doctors might have made a mistake. But now she knew it was hopeless. Yet even now he seemed no closer to death. He seemed to refuse to sink. When she first came into this dying ward she felt numb and afraid and wide open, as if the very cancer cells were floating everywhere. And when she first saw her father in bed he pulled her close and kissed her and she felt sickened and angry. It was as if he were trying to infect her with the disease. She wondered now how she could have thought this about her wonderful father.

He was a funny one. Sometimes if you weren't looking when he spoke to you he would forcibly turn your head round towards him.

He stirred again and opened his eyes, looked directly at her but without comprehending, without recognising. The eyes were opaque and bloodshot and rather wild. They terrified her.

She lightly held his shoulder and he opened his mouth as if gasping. She then held a glass of water to his lips and tilted it upward as he drained the liquid down.

"Dad! It's me."

"Forgive me. I was so lonely." His eyes were clearer now.

"Of course I forgive you." And as she stroked his forehead she remembered that she had forgotten to kiss Michael goodnight.

"A man is a man. A man is only human." He was straining his face as if he were bearing down, as if he were trying to pass motion or rid himself of pain.

"A man is — *Ach* —" Then a great expression of self disgust.

Suddenly she became aware of his disintegration. In that split second she compared him with the day when he was first admitted. When he walked into the hospital beside her, a puffing little bent figure insisting on carrying his own suitcase. The change had been gradual, every day a little bit more of him had been eaten away.

Every day he slept more, every day he dreamed more, every day he became more and more confused with his visions and reality. Maybe it was just as well. Perhaps it was nature's way of easing him into the hereafter.

She looked closely into his eyes. "Dad! Dad. Wake up sleepy head."

Then suddenly he became himself. His eyes clicked and

switched on. Then, miraculously transformed, he sat up. "Sophie. *Sophie!* How are you girl?"

He kissed her. The usual wet kiss, the kiss that had crippled her face for the forty odd years of her life. The kiss that brought the full weight and the sting of his consistently badly shaved chin.

She rubbed some cold cream on and then powdered her smarting skin. The usual ritual at every meeting.

Now came the telling off. She had learned to pretend to listen, to smile and nod and never defend herself.

"Why are you late? You should never be late — Haven't I been a good father —?" His voice droned on.

She preferred him now in that other state, in that dazed world where she could feel only sorrow for him. Sophie was always amazed at the speed in which he could travel between the two conditions. Only a moment before he had been looking closely at her hand, turning it over and over as if it were some strange object made out of wood or stone. Now — Snap! He was back in this world with a vengeance. Demanding, threatening. "If you do not bring my clothes —"

"How are you Dad?"

"How should I be? I want to go home."

"I've got some lovely things for you."

He pulled her close as if to tell her something of exceptional secrecy. His eyes darted to and fro as his mouth tried to form words. "When your mother died Sophie — I must tell you — When your mother died I went up West."

"I've got some first grade smoked salmon." She knew what was coming and she didn't want to know. She hated discussing sexual matters, especially with her own father. And particularly the things he wanted to get off his chest. She tried to pull away but he held on to her. "Sophie, I was lonely —"

"Dad, I don't want to know." She knew exactly where he went once a week, as soon as he got his pension from the post office.

She quickly unpacked the carrier bag. Out came the little paper bags which contained the various items of nosh. A few black olives, the smoked salmon, the fillets of herring, the double cream cheese, a pickled green cucumber, the Vienna rolls and the cheesecake.

She made him a sandwich, using almost a quarter of a pound of smoked salmon between two slices of rye bread. "This cost

219

almost eight shillings, this sandwich." She said, more to herself, as she pushed it into his hand.

"What's this? What's this?" He said with disgust. The hand holding the sandwich was stretched as far as possible from his body.

"It's the best smoked salmon. Eight shillings a quarter pound." She replied with a persecuted wail.

His hand immediately shot to his mouth and he was soon entirely occupied with the task of consuming the sandwich.

To her great relief he had seemed to forget the whole sordid subject of his sexual adventures.

"Sorry girl. Beautiful salmon." Then miraculously he was silent for a few moments.

Sophie was glad that he was in this place. The nuns were angels. They cared. This hospital had a marvellous name and no wonder. They had been marvellous to her father.

The last hospital he had been in could not compare to this place. The last place had been quite another story.

Only eight weeks before he had been admitted into the chronic ward of that other hospital. And after a month of bitter crying, she and his second wife relented and let him discharge himself. They promised the doctors they would look after him and care for him until the end. But of course it was impossible. Dying people were impossible.

In that other hospital the chronic sick were merely lumps of decaying demanding flesh. How he had cried. How pitiously. How he had clung to her all through those visiting hours sobbing into her coat. And even if his stories of the nurses' persecution were not true, he imagined they were.

Yet even if they were true, she could even understand their attitude. For in the chronic ward there was no return. All people liked to see some return for their work, but in the chronic ward, people just came and went, came and went. Surely those nurses must have hated the dying. For who could be more hateful than the old, chronic sick?

Sophie even brought the matter up with one of the night sisters. "We treat your father like everyone else. Everyone is treated with the utmost care and regard." The hard bitch face yapped.

Yes, Sophie had to admit that the chronic ward must seem like a punishment block for most nurses.

But here at least he would die amongst those who really cared. Here people were more than just decaying lumps of flesh to be shoved into the ground as quickly as possible. Here they believed in the divine purpose of existence.

She had to admit that she never liked nuns. She had always thought that they had not faced up to life. But now she knew how kind and gentle they could be. Only angels would be able to smile and be calm in the continual presence of Joseph Levene.

He finished the sandwich and the brief respite was over. "Why were you late? Why are you always late?"

"'I got everything you asked for."

"Why are you late then?"

It was a smiling matter, really. She came every day. Never once had she missed visiting him, and never once did he miss the opportunity of telling her off. The others hardly ever came. Yet if they actually found time to visit him, once in a blue moon, he was all smiles. To them he would never once say an unkind word.

There was a moral in this somewhere, she knew. But she also knew that she couldn't go against her nature. She had to come every day even though she hated all the responsibility falling upon her shoulders.

"Parents after all are parents. You must honour them." She told herself and her children so many times and especially recently.

She didn't want to think about her brothers and sisters, but at least it gave her an escape from his droning voice. Yet she did want to think about them. Sophie didn't want thanks; only perhaps a little appreciation. How many times had she told them over the phone? How many times had she tried to drum some common decency into them? "After all, he is your father."

Barry was always persuasive, was always able to twist her words and make her feel guilty for bringing the matter up in the first place.

How many times had Barry been? Once at the most. Was it even once? He had a fast car but he was too busy. The whole world was too busy while her father died. And Manny. All right, so he was in Israel. But not even a postcard; just one telegram seven weeks ago expressing regret. "Saddened by news. Terrible blow. Letter following. Manny."

Even if he flew home for a few days? Would that be too much to ask of him?

221

Then there was Ruth. Ruth with her afternoons drinking tea in Hampstead Garden Suburb raising money for Israel. All Ruth could afford a dying father was one lousy visit a week.

Sophie held her father's hand and wondered what had happened to them all. What had gone wrong? How thick they used to be. There was not another family in the world that was so close. Everybody spoke about it. In those days when everybody spoke.

Yet suddenly they had all drifted. The family had shattered, had scattered. There was still the pretence of closeness; she and Ruth still maintained daily contact on the telephone, but somehow it wasn't the same. From the day her mother died it wasn't the same. The family had died. They had just all refused to admit the death and bury it.

Sophie felt cold and afraid. She didn't relish this idea of the break-up. It was true she had her children and her Sam, but what else was there to hold on to? To hold on to one thing was no good. To place all your hopes and dreams and love on one object was dangerous. A family was more than a husband and children. A family was more than relatives all going their own sweet way. A family meant you were attached and not so lonely. A family meant you shared and were involved with each other's sorrow and joy. Somehow, these days, the joy was easily shared, but the sorrow was your own. Nobody wanted to know anymore.

And years ago people all lived near each other. Now they all lived miles apart. Ruth in H.G.S. A lovely house though, costing twenty-five thousand pounds. Marvellous. And Barry! He lived in Hampstead. Where else? She asked herself. He lived there with an arty girl. Nice, by the sound of her voice on the phone. He was also doing all right for himself. Hampstead was just his cup of coffee and she could just see him there with his Coffee House Cronies.

And she lived in Tottenham. Everyone was doing all right now, thank you very much. They didn't have to worry about the rent or food or anything like that. And these were the days they longed for. The times they schemed and dreamed towards.

She shook her head as she smiled. The good times were the bad times, as far as the family was concerned.

"Maybe I can't carry five or six pounds of potatoes. Maybe only two or three."

222

She heard her father going on. What then had happened to the family? She asked herself this over and over again. How many times had she lain awake all night, obsessed by the same question? What had gone wrong? Why? She knew when it happened. That was easy. When her mother died. But why?

Yet sometimes she thought that it wasn't as black as she painted it. Probably it was a matter of mere geography. You couldn't blame people if they wanted to move out where the air was cleaner. She knew she would move like a shot from Tottenham; if she could afford to.

She hated Tottenham. First of all there weren't that many Jewish people around. And at night the streets were dead. There was no life in the streets. No boys and girls flirted at the corner. And you never heard laughter. Even indoors. Kids didn't make fun for themselves anymore. They just sat with their eyes glued to the little box; their poor tiny red eyes fighting to stay open and then they'd drop to sleep on the floor or the settee. But that wasn't only Tottenham. But still she hated, hated Tottenham.

But what could you do? How long had she been on the housing list? Who wouldn't have jumped at such a lovely little flat? After all, home was where you made it.

But things were changed. There was never time to enjoy anything; everything was speeded up. Life was a fast rut. Even the Co-op had become a superstore. There was never time anymore for a good old chinwag. In and out, quickly, home with the biscuits that the kids wanted. The ones they sang jingles about on the telly. But even so they tasted nice.

"Did you hear me? Sophie? Did you? Did you?" He tugged her sleeve.

"Yes," she replied.

"So what will you do?" His eyes were alight with childlike expectancy.

"I'm — not sure." She then wondered what he had been asking of her.

"The children of today. Wasn't I always a good father? — Didn't —"

She nodded as her mind drifted away again.

It was just as well that she had her work cut out, what with the kids and Sam and the housework and with one thing and another. Because it didn't do to spend too much time worrying about what went wrong with the family. After all you had to live your life. You had to carry on for the sake of the kids. And Sam. He was a boy in a million. Everyone said so. He hated his work but he hardly ever complained. Once in a blue moon he might suddenly say "If only I could give this up. If only I could graft another way."

She saw him now, leaving the flat again, his bent-over figure trudging towards the shed where his Cortina was garaged. She always waved to him, without fail, but he could never wave back because his hands were on the wheel. But he always smiled as he drove away. One in a million. Then the kids off to school. Tears as usual. And then the work. The whole house to do and then the ironing and washing and the shopping and so much to do. Yes, it was just as well. Then the kids home. Already? And tea and the telly and Sam and supper and kids to bed. Then bed. Goodnight Darling! Goodnight.

No, the weekdays weren't so bad. It was the weekends and the nights when all the questions piled up.

"You'll never learn the things I've already forgotten." His thick voice brought her back to the ward. Then his words penetrated. She laughed; it was impossible not to laugh at such terrible arrogance.

"Things so delicate they slip the mind for the moment." He continued. And then he sat up with such energy that again she found it hard to believe that he had the complaint that they said he had. "That candlestick! I said to her pawn anything but not that. Know what she did?"

Sophie nodded, she had heard this story, word for word, detail by detail, every day for so many years. "I know what she did." Sophie said.

"No you don't. 'I'd even pawn my faith to feed my kids.' That's what she said. As if I didn't care if you went without."

Sophie knew that her father would die with the story of the candlestick on his lips. Year in and year out the retelling of the story had not abated; for years she had heard the endless argument going on through the thin walls, and when her mother died, every day he chose another child to drive mad with the same relentless words.

"Mind you, she was a woman in a million. We loved each other."

It was true. They did, and that argument of the candlestick was their only argument; it gave them renewed contact every day. It was like their oldest child who had never left home.

"So why were you late?"

"Buses." She shrugged. She wondered how long he could live. How long she could bear going there and watching him die. When he died the family would be dead and buried. He was the element that held the loose strands together. This little man noshing away at his double cream cheese sandwich held the life and death of the family within his own grasp and when that heart stopped and when that grip slackened they would all go their own sweet ways. And that would be that.

Sophie didn't think she could survive that. She needed contact with her brothers and her sister, she needed contact with the past. But she knew it was no use. All her love, all her love for all of them would not be enough. All her love and tears and concern would never be enough to raise and mend the broken remains of the family when the grip of the father failed.

"I must go home. Please take me to my home. This cream cheese is not as good as the other day."

She thought about that time when he was between wives, when he went out on Friday afternoons. At first she hadn't guessed, not until that evening when her favourite uncle came.

"Out again is he? Guess where he is." Her favourite uncle laughed and winked and she wanted to be sick. She did not look at her father full in the face for nearly a month after that. She shivered when he sat at the table to eat with them; this wrinkled old man with his sexual appetite.

For he came to live with her, between wives. She was the only one who seemed to want to take him. All the others had their excuses. It always fell on her.

So she took him in. But she knew she deserved no medals, for after all he was her father. It was the least she could do, even if life did become hell from that moment on.

First he just sat numbed from Sarah's death, far away in thought, his face a perpetual waterfall from tears. She virtually had to lead him to the lavatory, otherwise he might have done it on the armchair. Then, when he emerged from his daze, he started to watch their every movement and he never stopped nagging and criticising and he caused endless arguments. He became a third child whose favourite game was to create as much unhappiness as possible.

Yet when nature overtook grief things did get better. When

she got over the first shock of her father prowling after prostitutes she had to admit that life was more tolerable.

When he returned late on Friday night, after the Sabbath was in, only then would she light the candles and start the Friday night meal of *lokshen* soup and fried fish.

How well she remembered those Friday nights. The children happy and clean and late to bed because of no school tomorrow, and Sam all shaved and talkative, and her father silent, his neck slumped forward, his hands behind his back and his eyes fighting to stay open. Once he fell so fast asleep during the meal that she and Sam had to carry him bodily to his bed and undress him; while the kids giggled in the doorway to see such a funny sight.

"How is my dear wife? I mean — how is my wife? How is Auntie Tilly? Is she better? Is she coming?" His voice cut across her thoughts.

Sophie shrugged in such a way that it could have meant anything.

The subject of her stepmother always affected her deeply. She didn't know why she hated the old woman. She should have been delighted that day when he came and told her he was marrying again. "After all — it's nearly two years since the stone setting." He said guiltily, realising that she was hurt. She should have rejoiced but she only felt incredible anger. And hatred. Now she knew that on that day her mother truly died. And that day the family started dying.

He had met Auntie Tilly at some old people's club that he went to every Wednesday afternoon; one of those places where old people go for tea and chat, and do nothing but argue amongst themselves and boast of their grandchildren.

Then he brought the old lady back one afternoon. "Tilly I want you to meet my favourite." He said. She remembered rushing into the other room and bursting into tears. But they didn't notice.

"Didn't you hear me? How is your Auntie Tilly?" He said again.

Sophie hated the name 'Auntie Tilly', the name stuck in her throat, she loathed using it. "Your wife — is still ill, so I believe or so she says, on the phone. And she is not coming. The same as I told you yesterday."

Although there was no comparison with the old woman and her dead mother she could not help trying to compare. Her mother had dignity, grace, but this old woman — well maybe it wasn't her fault that she couldn't even speak twenty words of English.

Even if she had lived in England for forty odd years; after all she was a foreign Jew, from Russia, and they were different. True, her father was from Poland but he was a special case; he was more like an English Jew despite his strange ways. But her mother was born in England. Now that was a mixture; the Jewish soul and the English manner. Such a combination you could be proud of.

All the others were pleased when he married again. They all said "Sophie, good for you. You take everything on yourself." Each in turn took her to one side to say how much they worried about her; how they would have loved to have put him up if only they had the room. Despite the fact that they all had twice as much room as she. "Sophie — you're a miracle. Don't know how you put up with it."

They were all pleased for her but none of them knew the bitterness and the pain that she felt inside.

There was a small wedding party and then suddenly he was gone from her flat. And she missed him. She actually missed him.

He moved to a small two storey house near Stamford Hill where his new wife already rented two rooms.

She saw him after that once a week. On Saturday morning he would come and always say exactly the same thing. "I loved your mother. Only your mother. I was lonely." It was as if he were asking her to forgive him.

So he stopped his weekly Soho search and settled in with Auntie Whatyoumaycallit and they argued incessantly. But in this respect she couldn't blame the old lady. And there he lived until the day when she took him for a medical check because he kept on complaining of having a terrible pain in the back.

And here he was. "Your mother, God rest her dear soul, would never let me stay with nuns." With great disgust he almost spat out the final word. "Ill or not she would have taken me home in a tick."

It was true. And Sophie was pleased that at last he seemed to acknowledge the great gap that separated his first and second wives. But her stepmother was ill, there was no doubt about

227

that; she wasn't even well enough to look after herself. One had to be fair. Yet her own mother would have crawled around on the floor, losing blood, before she'd let him cry away his last few days in a *Goyisher* hospital.

He lit his pipe and a great gust of smoke billowed forth. She turned her head away and tried to stifle the immediate coughing. She remembered how for years he had driven them all berserk with that disgusting horrible shag. Even on the way to the hospital he drove her mad to go upstairs in the bus so that he could light up. Then when he was finally admitted she just let him puff away.

"You don't complain suddenly," he said, and she was surprised he even noticed, hoped he wouldn't get suspicious and was relieved to see him smile. He had obviously imagined that for once, and at last, his children were beginning to respect him and his few pleasures.

It was strange that he didn't know he was going to die. Maybe he did know. Maybe he didn't want them to know that he knew. She rejected this almost as soon as she thought it up. No, he obviously did not know. The doctor on that terrible day even asked her whether he should tell the old man.

"No. No. Mustn't tell him." She cried hysterically and then came out of the room trying to hold back the tears, trying to smile. He didn't even notice that. "What did the doctor want to speak about?"

"You've got to stay in, for a rest and a check up."

"You sure it's nothing serious?" It was the nearest he got to anxiety.

"Course not. It's the old prostate trouble. A few weeks at the most." And he believed her. He was the most gullible man on God's earth.

"So how are the kids? How's my Michael boy? And Sam? Plenty work?" His questions brought her back to the present. But she could see that he wasn't interested in her reply.

"Fine. Mustn't grumble." She looked round towards the entrance. Possibly one of the others might come, one of them might actually condescend to put in an appearance. A minor miracle might occur and she would not have to bear the brunt alone.

Joe screwed up his face as if experiencing the most excruciating pain.

"Dad! What's up? Pain?"

228

But he popped a chunk of cheesecake into his mouth and licked his fingers. "Pain? For why pain? I'm better."

"Stop screwing up your face then."

"I'm practising, for my enemies, to scare them away."

"You haven't got an enemy in the world." She said with some pride.

"No enemies?" He answered incredulously "What about Uncle Walter?"

Still it went on; the interwoven fantasies and intrigues and threats of brothers, aunts and uncles and sisters and second cousins and nephews and sisters. "She said that. Three years ago — may I drop down dead on this spot — she said that I said that he knew that she said — may I spit blood if I tell a lie — and you know what he did? And what I said when he did what he did? — May the ground open up and swallow me — as God is my witness — know what I did? No you don't — Know what I did? I never forgave him, because my second cousin Lew said to that *momser* Benny — may he lack salt —"

Sophie had learned long ago to stop her ears without the use of fingers. She had heard all this ever since she started to walk. The skeletons were not in the cupboards in the Levene family; they were all sitting around the table, playing cards. Rattling, arguing, nagging, coveting.

No. No-one would come now; it was too late. They were usually on time if they came at all.

"Please let me come to your home then." His plaintive cry made her feel so dreadfully sorry for him.

"You know I haven't got room. The kids are growing up."

"Let me sleep on your floor."

She cried, and loathed him for making such a request.

He knew exactly her weak spot. How could she refuse him the floor? And once inside the house how could she refuse him the bed? But she knew she had to refuse. She could not bear watching him die in her flat. She could not bear to have the children around and the very walls witnessing his last screams. She could not bear her flat soaking in such sounds and sights of agony.

When he was dead she would change. She had to. She prayed for change. For the time when she would not be able to cry. A lot of things would happen to her in life; a lot of painful things; watching the kids growing up and making mistakes and leaving home and then their lives to worry about. She wanted to harden herself, to prepare herself for the onslaught of the years. That was her prayer. She stopped crying. "I'm afraid you cannot leave the hospital yet. And that is that!"

He whimpered. Sophie wondered how her mother had managed to put up with such a man for so many years. She must have loved him a lot. Then, strangely, as if she had communicated her thoughts, he said "When your mother died — I died."

"That's not exactly true. You married again." She was ashamed to feel so much bitterness towards a dying man. But he never seemed to recognise inflections.

To this day he hadn't suspected even one iota of her overwhelming bitterness towards the remarriage. If only he had acted like a father. If only when her mother died he had withdrawn and waited decently for his own death; if only he had stayed home with the children and gone quiet and retold old stories of childhood; of old days in Poland; of little incidents and memories of grandparents. If only he would have mellowed she would have had that to remember him by. That would have been nice. She would have liked that.

He seemed to drift away again. The food and the paper bags were pushed to one side and his eyes were going peculiarly right up into his head. He seemed to be smiling, to be in some form of ecstasy; yet still tried to hold on to the world with a few sporadic words. He swayed gently backwards and forwards and clutched her arm tight as he spoke. "So — so — how's the kids? Yes — I asked — Natalie? Big girl now? — So — where were we? Yes — you said the buses — Vitamins! Fat lot of good. Not a prisoner. Respect."

She smoothed his brow and he closed his eyes and she gently pushed him backwards until his head lay on the pillow.

He liked that. He loved his daughter. Sophie. She was the best of the bunch. They were all good children but Sophie was the best. She was an angel. He could hear his own voice again, but he wasn't sure if it came from inside or outside him.

"I keep on remembering the past. All my life swims in front of me. Who taught my life to swim? I never learned. I'm content now. And why not? Didn't I work hard enough?

A man who worked hard all his life deserved a rest now and again. And if the mind wanders — well, let it, go with it. You don't need a visa this way. And it won't cost a penny. Funny, as you get older you remember the strangest things."

230

Joe could see the pair of boots again. The tiny pair of boots. His first pair of boots. He knew he could touch them if he tried but he felt a little too tired to reach forward, for the moment. Maybe he would in a while; meanwhile he was content just to look at them.

Yet he was running in slow motion, as in a dream, each step springing him higher and higher into the air until he was floating away from the hospital.

He could hear children singing, either in the streets or in school, but he wanted to return to earth and reach the boots, and clean them and put them on and lace them. He dived down into darkness towards the one lighted place in the world.

"Look Mother, I can tie the knot now." His mother smiled but he could not get the shoes on; they were not within the grasp of his quickly searching hands.

The one lighted place was twenty square feet of Warsaw. He could hear chickens. "The first time I went to school I cried when you left me." But he knew that he was not talking to his mother. It was Sophie who was there. His daughter. Although she was not yet born.

He was not yet old enough to tie his boots, he was still a child waving goodbye to his mother. Her hand soothed his forehead. He was afraid of the dark. Afraid of the coats on the door and the open cupboards. But she pushed away the night fears and the day fears. Almost as quickly as she gave him those fears. He could see that now.

"Don't be afraid of the streets. Don't be afraid. Eat up. Don't wander out. Never. Promise. Lace up your boots and go to school. Straight to school. Don't talk to anyone."

He was older now. He stopped crying. He wandered. He was seven. Seven years and something — No he was almost eight by now. Because already he started wandering. He reached out into Warsaw, darted along the narrow streets, gazed into lighted windows, rushed across the market place. There near the hospital where the stalls were full of peardrops and fish and shoes, all the bells were ringing. Each peal shivered through his bones, made him feel sick.

Soldiers prayed at the bleeding feet of Christ. The nuns of Warsaw were drawing blood again. In the night they came with needles and glass to steal the blood of sleeping children, to paint the feet of their white wooden statues. There was smoke in the open door where people were on their knees and murmuring. The candles sent up gusts of yellow smoke and stank.

"Come home. Don't wander. Tie your laces and hurry home." Her voice boomed across the sky, through the ghetto, over the fishmarket. "Joseph! Joseph! It's getting dark."

The sky closed down. He fled without boots across the whole of Warsaw, chased by the eyes of the Jew-haters, whose hands fortunately at this moment were clasped together in prayer, and there-

231

*fore were not free to clutch his throat and tear it open and pull out
his heart and burn it. He passed through Jerusalem Street and
prayed quickly as he ran.*

"Shemah Yisroel — Adoni — Allehanu — Adoni—"

*And suddenly he was in boots. He was running in his first pair
of shining boots and the laces were tied in a double knot and all
the bells of Warsaw sang and the fish from the stalls flew back
into the Vistula and Jerusalem Street went dark and his mother
soothed his brow. He lay on the bed. She had removed his boots.
He reached out for them again but his fingers groped through air.*

"Dad! Dad! Guess who's here?" She mopped his wet forehead as
she eagerly looked towards the ward entrance.

"Dad! Dad! Barry's here."

His daughter was speaking. He sat up. Sophie was speaking.
It was not his mother at all, but his beautiful daughter, the best
of the bunch. Sophie. Named after his mother and almost as fat.
And certainly as fat as the beautiful carp that swam in the zinc
bath on Friday afternoon.

"Dad. Guess who's here."

Once more he came back into himself and noticed that his
daughter was standing up and looking away from the bed. Then
the meaning of her words dawned upon him. "What? Barry here.
My Barry boy is here?"

He tried to focus his eyes upon the corridor. Yes, he could see
him, he could just about see his own smart and youngest son.
The architect. The clever one. "So Barry came." Joe settled back
into his bed with satisfaction.

"Why doesn't he come straight in then? What's he doing out
there?" Sophie said, but then she noticed that Barry had brought
the girl. So he finally had decided to introduce his future wife to
the family. She waved to her brother, flapping her hand furiously, but he, in return, indicated that he had to stay outside for
the moment.

"So where is he then?" Joe took up his pipe and lit it.

"Probably going to talk to the doctor."

"Doctor? Doctor? What for?"

"To see how you're getting on, of course," she replied.

So Barry had finally managed to drag himself to Hackney and
now he was going to speak to the doctor, to show off his posh
accent and try and show everyone how concerned he was for his
father.

Sophie felt the blood rushing to her head. "So he finally con-descended. So he finally found his way." She sat down again and did not return the handsome smile that her brother flashed across to her.

"Relax! Relax Sophie! That's your trouble, you're too excitable. So my Barry came to see me." The old man pinched her cheek and then leaned back and put the earphones on. He felt very calm now as he puffed on his pipe.

"Don't I have the best children in the world? And why not? Don't I deserve it? Didn't I work hard enough all my life? Haven't I always been a good father?"

She nodded as she boiled inside.

His face lit up, because the music coming through the ear-phones agreed with him. And for no reason he remembered how proud he was the day he first tied his own bootlaces.

Whatever Happened to Isaac Babel?

Whatever happened to Isaac Babel?
And if it comes to that —
whatever happened to those old men of Hackney
who sat around a wireless, weeping tears of pride
at weather forecasts from Radio Moscow?

Whatever happened to us? The Lovers of Peace?
And to our proud banners?
Whatever happened to our son?
And to that Picasso dove of Peace
we brought him back from Budapest?

Whatever happened to that little man
who tried to leap above himself?
He had a fire in his eyes;
a certain beauty in his eyes.
Or maybe that was merely poverty.

Whatever happened to Vladimir
Mayakovsky? Sergei Esenin? And Leon Trotsky?
Between the Instant Quaker and the Colour Supplement
we are apt to find no time to talk of them.

But then, we are apt to find no time to talk.

Now it is day,
and rather late in the day.
Whatever happened to us?

We are the worm contractors;
lusty youths of fire have become tweeded teachers,
with a swish Hi-fi that was bought for cash
and a smashing collection of Protest Songs.

Oh ye dreamers of peace!
Dreamers of bright red dawn!
Whatever happened to that dream?

From *Erica, I Want to Read You Something* (1967)

234

The dead are buried and the years
and forests of computers cover us.
We are crushed within the heart.
We are gone like prophet Leon
with ice-picks in our brain.

But there is no red stain.

We leave nothing behind
except volumes and volumes; such beautiful volumes.
Unread but rather splendidly
displayed upon tasteful teak.

Oh ye sitters down for peace!
Only the pigeons protest
these days down Whitehall.
Oh Comrades of Slogan Square!
This is a windy Judas corner;
this is the fraught, frozen-over winter park.

I smile and walk backward.
If you insist I am also part of this.
But through my clenched teeth
I somehow cannot stop myself chanting.

Whatever happened to Isaac Babel?
Whatever became of me?

I think often of Isaac Babel,
of his unsung death.
And as I walk away from you
I know that I am all full up.
I am all full up with people.
I have no vacancies.

Suicide at forty would be mere exhibitionism.

Besides, I have songs to sing.
Songs for myself;
songs to keep me warm;
songs to feed into mouths.
And I have one mouth in particular to kiss;
and eyes above that mouth from where I draw my songs.
He was a funny little man, Isaac Babel.
And one would have thought him a nonentity,
had they not needed to dispose of him
so thoroughly in the dark.

Most people in this world are worthwhile;
therefore I can dispense with most of them.

You have to draw the line somewhere.

Yes, I think often of that little man
"with glasses on his nose and Autumn in his heart".
Isaac Babel! Can you hear me?
I think often of your untelevised death.

Whatever happened to us
Returning from Whitehall
our banners smudged with rain,
our slogans running away?
Us waving, shaving, running after
our going youth and euphoria.
Hurtling through these fattening years
of hollow laughter.

And incidentally — who are we and
where are we?

So dreams die.
My dreams.
So can you blame me for building
barricades in West Hampstead?
Nice flat. Garden flat; unnumbered,
somewhere behind the Finchley Road.

With children laughing and children crying
and within me still one thread of longing.
And one wife calm and warm, belonging.

So — where was I?
Oh yes! Whatever happened to —
What was his name?

Never mind, nothing really changes;
except children grow,
and we realise there is nowhere else to go.
There is only us now. Us alone.

And not forgetting that rather funny
little Jewish Cossack fellow
who at the moment slips the mind.
Not to worry, they're bound to know his name
in Better Books.

There is a certain joy in knowing;
but then again a certain peace and quiet in
half forgetting.

East End titles from Five Leaves

East End Jewish Radicals 1875-1914
William J Fishman
336 pages, 0907123457, £14.99

East End 1888
William J Fishman
407 pages, 0907123856, £14.99

The London Years
Rudolf Rocker
304 pages, 0907123309, £14.99

Choose Your Frog
Harold Rosen (poetry)
36 pages, 090712335X, £4.50

Fisherdorf and Other Poems (forthcoming)
Dual language — Yiddish and English
AN Stencl
96 pages, 1905512236, £7.99

From bookshops, or, post free, from
Five Leaves Publications,
PO Box 8786, Nottingham
NG1 9AW